"This book does a mar[...] [...]tions between Asperger's and A[...] [...] has much to offer to mental he[...]

Fred R. V[...] [...] [...]niatry, Chu[...] [...] [...] University School of Medicine; editor, Encyclopedia of Autism; editor-in-chief, Journal of Autism and Developmental Disorders

"I read your book and really like all the case histories of adults, young adults, and children. It will provide valuable insights to parents and teachers."

Temple Grandin, PhD, professor of animal science, Colorado State University; author, The Autistic Brain and Thinking in Pictures-My Life with Autism

"This well-written and informative book draws upon research and Dr. Brown's extensive clinical experience to fill a great need for clinicians, patients, and families. It presents clinical cases of highly intelligent people struggling with both ADHD and Asperger Syndrome (high functioning autism spectrum disorder). It wisely informs us of what they can do to improve their quality of life. I congratulate Dr. Brown for this unique book that serves a neglected population of people."

Russell A. Barkley, PhD, clinical professor of psychiatry, Medical University of South Carolina

"Drawing on his many decades of clinical work and meticulous research, Brown shows us the talents and strengths in this widely misunderstood group of children and adults. A major contribution, a beautiful book!"

Edward M. Hallowell, MD, author, New York Times bestseller Driven to Distraction as well as Delivered from Distraction and ADHD.2.0.

"Asperger's syndrome and ADHD often combine to create a complex profile of abilities. I recommend this informative and practical book for professionals and for parents."

Tony Attwood, PhD, clinical psychologist and associate professor, Griffith University, Queensland, Australia; author of The Complete Guide to Asperger's Syndrome

"Dr. Thomas Brown has crafted a superb and widely accessible book focused on smart children and adults with ADHD who have specific strengths and interests, but who also encounter significant difficulties in social and school settings. This volume is well worth reading by clinicians, educators, and parents as well as those brilliant individuals dealing with Asperger's syndrome."

James F. Leckman, MD, PhD, *Nelson Harris Professor of Child Psychiatry, Pediatrics and Psychology, Yale University*

"This book is a must read for mental health professionals, educators, and families interested in understanding the intersection between ADHD and Asperger Syndrome. A masterful storyteller, Brown uncovers the "central mystery of ADHD" and provides a science-based understanding within the framework of beautifully articulated stories of daily life in those overcoming challenges of ADHD with Asperger Syndrome."

Elizabeth A. Laugeson, PsyD, *associate clinical professor of Psychiatry and Behavioral Sciences, UCLA Semel Institute; author of* The Science of Making Friends; *founder and director of the UCLA PEERS Clinic for individuals with social impairments*

"*ADHD and Asperger Syndrome* is a great challenge in clinical evaluation, diagnosis and treatment. In 12 case examples rich in details Dr. Brown shows how to help these children, teens and adults. This book will be beneficial for their families and friends as well as for mental health professionals."

Yufeng Wang, PhD, *professor of Psychology, Peking University, Sixth Hospital Institute of Mental Health, Peking China; editor-in-Chief:* Chinese Handbook of Attention Deficit/Hyperactivity Disorder

"Very bright students with ADHD and Asperger's are not uncommon at MIT and other colleges. Dr. Brown's scientific, yet very empathic discussion of the struggles of these students is a valuable gift to the students, their faculty, their clinicians and their families."

Xiaolu Hsi, PhD, *clinical neuropsychologist, Student Mental Health Service, Massachusetts Institute of Technology, Massachusetts Mental Health Center, Harvard Medical School*

"Thomas Brown is a master at using vibrant story-telling to deliver cutting-edge research. His new book reminds us that all those with autism are not the same. *ADHD and Asperger Syndrome in Smart Kids and Adults* provides insights and understanding parents need to more effectively support their complex kids with ADHD, Asperger Syndrome, or both."

Elaine Taylor-Klaus, CPCC, PCC, *CEO of ImpactParents.com*; author of Essential Guide to Raising Complex Kids with ADHD, Anxiety, and More

ADHD and Asperger Syndrome in Smart Kids and Adults

ADHD and Asperger Syndrome in Smart Kids and Adults offers detailed examples of individuals who have above-average cognitive intelligence, but struggle with executive function impairments of ADHD and significant social-emotional impairments of Asperger syndrome.

The book centers around twelve case studies of bright children, teens, and adults treated for both ADHD and Asperger syndrome. Each chapter describes diverse examples of their strengths and their difficulties, and explains how these individuals can be helped with appropriate treatment to overcome their ADHD impairments and to improve their ability to understand and interact more effectively with others. Case examples are followed by updated, science-based descriptions of these disorders.

Providing science-based information about ADHD and Asperger syndrome in clearly understandable, accessible language, this text is ideal for clinicians, educators, social workers, medical and mental health service providers, and parents of those struggling with such impairments. It also advocates for restoring the diagnosis of Asperger syndrome to diagnostic manuals of the American Psychiatric Association and World Health Organization.

Thomas E. Brown, PhD, earned his doctorate in clinical psychology at Yale University and served on Yale faculty for 20 years. He has published six books on ADHD and now directs the Brown Clinic for Attention & Related Disorders in Manhattan Beach, CA.

ADHD and Asperger Syndrome in Smart Kids and Adults

Twelve Stories of Struggle, Support, and Treatment

Thomas E. Brown

Routledge
Taylor & Francis Group

NEW YORK AND LONDON

First published 2022
by Routledge
605 Third Avenue, New York, NY 10158

and by Routledge
2 Park Square, Milton Park, Abingdon, Oxon OX14 4RN

Routledge is an imprint of the Taylor & Francis Group, an informa business

Library of Congress Cataloging-in-Publication Data
Names: Brown, Thomas E., 1942- author.
Title: ADHD and Asperger syndrome in smart kids and adults : twelve stories of struggle, support, and treatment / Thomas E. Brown.
Description: New York : Routledge, 2021. | Includes bibliographical references and index.
Identifiers: LCCN 2020052747 (print) | LCCN 2020052748 (ebook) | ISBN 9780367694913 (hardback) | ISBN 9780367694906 (paperback) | ISBN 9781003141976 (ebook)
Subjects: LCSH: Asperger's syndrome in children. | Attention-deficit-disordered children. | Attention-deficit hyperactivity disorder.
Classification: LCC RJ506.A9 B773 2021 (print) | LCC RJ506.A9 (ebook) | DDC 618.92/8589–dc23
LC record available at https://lccn.loc.gov/2020052747
LC ebook record available at https://lccn.loc.gov/2020052748

ISBN: 978-0-367-69491-3 (hbk)
ISBN: 978-0-367-69490-6 (pbk)
ISBN: 978-1-003-14197-6 (ebk)

DOI: 10.4324/9781003141976

Typeset in Baskerville
by Taylor & Francis Books

To my wife, Bobbie,
With love and gratitude for all you were,
all you gave, and all we shared together over 49 years.
T.E.B.

Contents

> This chapter excerpts the autobiographical writings of four
> extremely successful adults with Asperger syndrome. Included are: a
> boy who dropped out of school before eighth grade and later
> became a university professor of journalism who won a Pulitzer
> prize as an outstanding music critic; a woman trapped in feeling
> "nerdy, shy, and socially inappropriate," shed her shame to become
> a successful writer and publisher mentoring others seeking self-
> understanding; a high school dropout who engineered exploding
> guitars for the rock band KISS, who runs an auto repair shop, and
> wrote a *New York Times bestseller, Look me in the eye*; and a gifted animal
> scientist born with classical autism, now Asperger syndrome, who
> thinks in pictures, has designed one third of the livestock handling
> facilities in the U.S., has published six books, and lectures widely on
> autism.

Joshua suffered from severe social anxiety which required carefully
adjusted treatment with medication, but he also had considerable
difficulty from bullying by his peers. His parents repeatedly told
him that he was "gifted" and that his classmates were just jealous of
him. Much of his peer difficulty was reactive to his condescension
toward classmates. He was a gifted musician and functioned better
in a new school where he could be with other students involved in
music, but he needed considerable support to learn how to adapt
to peer culture.

Sam benefitted from participation in sports where he did quite
well, but he often antagonized peers and classmates by criticizing
their performance. His parents had chronic conflicts with one
another over how much to confront Sam with unacceptable
behavior vs. supporting him. They also needed help to avoid
giving him ineffective strategies for dealing with peers who teased
him.

Bella is a very bright and creative girl who distanced herself from
classmates and spent most of her free time playing video games.
She was terrified of the transition from middle school to high
school. She responded well to therapeutic role-playing sessions to
try out different ways of interacting with peers and to extra support
from a high school counselor who helped to prepare her for
transition to high school.

Jeremy's parents were struggling with marital conflict as well as
about how to deal with Jeremy's frequent problems with school.
When we began work together he was "on strike" in his classes
insisting that he would not cooperate with teachers until they
stopped the special education support services he found
humiliating. He also struggled with his conflicting loyalties for each
parent and his fear that he would become like his mentally ill
uncle. His mother's sudden onset of cancer complicated the family
dynamics and Jeremy's need for support.

Justin was socially isolated and would bang his head on school walls and leave the classroom anytime he made a mistake. Collaboration with his teachers helped set up interventions to avoid his maladaptive reactions to frustration. His grandmother brought him to her home daily after school to get his homework done. His family was initially fearful about using medications, but fine-tuned medication plus psychotherapy with Justin, his father and grandmother helped him improve his emotional disruptions, his schoolwork and interacting with peers. Psychotherapy also helped him to address his concerns about growth and sexuality.

Anthony was obsessed with his desire to develop a relationship with a girlfriend, but he lacked the ability to understand how she could be less enthused about her brief experience in dating him than he was. He lacked "theory of mind," the ability to understand and empathize with another person's point of view different from his own. Despite cautions from several friends and me, he continued to try to see her even after being served a restraining order. Only after being jailed for violating that order was he able to begin to understand what went wrong.

Drew had a long history being brilliant with computer science, but also maintaining an arrogant and defiant attitude toward his parents and many of his teachers, not caring about how others felt about him. His parents were unable to confront him effectively about this when he was in elementary school, high school or university. When he totally wrecked three cars in motor vehicle accidents, they bought him a new pickup truck and allowed him to use their credit card for a 3 month solo trip. He and his mother were unable to sustain treatment.

Sandra's inability to complete an undergraduate degree was due
largely to her chronic difficulties with a type of Obsessive-
Compulsive Disorder perfectionism combined with untreated
ADHD. However, Sandra also felt intense social anxiety and was
very fearful about growing up and separating from her mother. Her
emotional turmoil and underlying depression led to occasional
episodes of cutting herself which she described as a way to help
herself feel emotions that otherwise she could not experience. She
needed a writing tutor and a course of psychotherapy to develop
more self-acceptance and better understanding of her conflict.

Jorge had been diagnosed with ADHD, encopresis, and daytime
enuresis prior to his evaluation with me when he was 8 years old.
His parents were divorced and his mother home-schooled him
until eighth grade. A bitter dispute between his parents about
whether he should be treated with medication was resolved by the
court. With medication his schoolwork improved; he was placed in
a small private school where he did very well. For college, Jorge
moved to another state where he lived with his father and
eventually graduated with honors, despite continuing difficulties
with independent functioning and social interactions.

PART IV

Richard is extremely bright and was very successful in functioning
within the confines of the academic world of college and law
school, but he was not at all adept at managing social-emotional
interactions in the work setting with his superiors or with others on
the staff. He was unable to develop an adequate mentor
relationship with senior partners in either law firm. He was not
able to understand the importance of completing an assignment
his supervisor was depending on; he could not see the situation
from his supervisor's point of view. He had similar problems in
understanding the needs and expectations the girlfriend he was
living with.

Although she had been very successful in her schooling and in becoming an attorney despite some language processing problems, Loretta's 40th birthday was upsetting for her because she felt like a failure for having ended a 4 year engagement and for her inability to sustain emotional closeness to others. She struggled with intense ambivalence about social relationships and, like many other adults with Asperger syndrome, her ongoing conflicts over intimacy led to a significant depression in midlife.

Gary was able to relate comfortably with the students he was teaching and coaching, but he found it quite difficult to develop reciprocal relationships with people his own age. His relationship with the lesbian woman he met on the camp staff was his first experience in trying to develop a relationship with a woman. When that relationship was lost, he was devastated. The relationship he formed with another woman when he was with her as a patient on a psychiatric ward led quickly to their living together, getting married and having a child. Soon after the birth of his son the relationship between Gary and his wife deteriorated emotionally for both of them, but he was able to sustain strong involvement with his son.

The stereotype of ADHD as simply a behavior problem of little boys who are constantly restless and rarely listen to what others say or expect has been replaced with a science-based understanding of ADHD as a complex problem in the unfolding development of the brain's self- management system, its executive functions. This chapter explains that new understanding of ADHD, how it changes across development, and how it can be effectively treated.

Illustrations

Figure

Tables

About the Author

Thomas E. Brown is a clinical psychologist who earned his PhD from Yale University. He served on the clinical faculty of the Department of Psychiatry at the Yale School of Medicine for 20 years while also operating a clinic for children and adults with ADHD and related problems. In 2017 Dr. Brown relocated to California where he opened the Brown Clinic for Attention and Related Disorders in Manhattan Beach.

He is a skilled, empathic teacher/clinician. His 28-minute video "What is ADHD? Attention Deficit Disorder Explained" on YouTube has received rave reviews and more than 4 million views. Dr. Brown taught continuing medical education courses on ADHD for the American Psychiatric Association for twenty years and has given lectures and workshops in hospitals, medical schools, universities and for professional and advocacy groups throughout the U.S. and in more than 40 other countries.

He served as adjunct clinical associate professor of Psychiatry & Behavioral Sciences at the Keck School of Medicine of the University of Southern California and is an elected fellow of the American Psychological Association and the Society for Clinical Child and Adolescent Psychology.

Dr. Brown developed the Brown Executive Function/Attention Rating Scales (1996, 2019) and has published 30 articles in peer-reviewed journals. His award-winning book *Attention Deficit Disorders: The Unfocused Mind in Children and Adults* (Yale University Press, 2005) has been published in seven languages.

Dr. Brown has published six books on ADHD. His most recent are *Smart but Stuck: Emotions in Teens and Adults with ADHD* and *Outside the Box: Rethinking ADD/ADHD in Children and Adults: A Practical Guide*. His website is www.BrownADHD Clinic.com.

Acknowledgments

I am deeply grateful to each of the patients and families described in this book. They shared with me their struggles and the strengths they used to deal with them. In sharing their experiences, these people helped me to appreciate the wide variety of ways ADHD and Asperger syndrome can overlap, impact, and help individuals and families in different stages and circumstances of life. They also impressed me with their courage and persistence in trying to develop and sustain their relationships with those they love and who love them.

I am very grateful to my daughter, Liza, for her sustained support, assistance, and helpful comments over the two years of my writing this manuscript. She, my son Dave, my grandkids Noah and Simone, and my son-in-law Abel support me in countless ways with generous love, encouragement, and continuing sunshine, especially since the loss of my wife seven years ago.

I am also indebted to my colleague Dr. Ryan Kennedy, who has worked with me for eleven years. He does much to support my work and ongoing daily learning in our shared work with the children and adults who seek services in our clinic. Thanks also to Corrine Gach, our office manager, who supports and helps to keep me organized.

Thanks also to Amanda Devine, my editor, and to Grace McDonnell, editorial assistant, both of whom have provided generous assistance and support for this project. I am also grateful to Stacey Carter for coordinating production, to Hamish Ironside for careful copyediting, and to all others in the team at Routledge/Taylor & Francis who helped to complete this project and make it available to readers.

Introduction

The Story of Dan and the Purposes of This Book

I am a clinical psychologist. For more than twenty years I operated a specialty clinic in Connecticut for high-IQ children and adults with ADHD and related problems while I also served on the clinical faculty in Psychiatry at the Yale University School of Medicine. In 2017 I closed my Connecticut clinic and relocated it to Manhattan Beach, California where I now continue my work while living closer to my adult children and my grandchildren.

The reason I specialize in assessment and treatment of high-IQ children and adults is that I have found that many of those who are very bright and have ADHD and related problems often are not recognized as having those difficulties until quite late in their educational career. Meanwhile they often are criticized by parents, teachers, and themselves as lazy, unmotivated, or oppositional while they struggle with doing their academic work. Some give up and do not pursue the education they wanted and expected.

While at Yale I published scientific research articles on 157 high-IQ adults (Brown, 2009) and 117 high-IQ children and adolescents (Brown, Reichel, and Quinlan, 2011a), all of whom suffered with ADHD and were not identified until relatively late in their educational careers. Many of those patients performed well in their early years of schooling, but had increasing frustration and difficulties as they moved up into middle school, high school or university where they were faced with increasingly demanding work with far less support and direction from teachers or parents.

One problem that delays many of these very bright kids and adults from being recognized as having ADHD is that many parents, teachers, pediatricians, psychologists, and psychiatrists still hold an outdated view of ADHD as a simple problem of young children who are chronically hyperactive, unwilling to follow directions, and who often demonstrate significant behavior problems. Many clinicians and educators are not yet aware of the updated scientific understanding of ADHD as a usually inherited delay in development of the brain's complex self-management system, its "executive functions." They do not know that many of those with ADHD have never demonstrated significant hyperactivity or behavioral problems.

Another major problem that often masks the difficulties and failures of these very bright students is what I have described in journal articles and six different books as "the central mystery of ADHD." I use this term to refer to the fact that

DOI: 10.4324/9781003141976-1

every one of the several thousand patients I have evaluated and diagnosed with ADHD has one puzzling characteristic: each has a few tasks or activities in which they have virtually no difficulty in sustaining the focus, effort, organization, and self-control that they lack in almost all other tasks they undertake.

Most children, teens and adults who come to our clinic are quite smart; their tested intelligence is usually in the high average or superior range. They can focus their attention and efforts very well for a few tasks and activities that really interest them. Yet they are consistently frustrated because they are unable to focus and work effectively for most other tasks they need to do in school, work, and other activities. Many are found to have ADHD—chronic impairments in executive functions, the self-management system of the brain. These difficulties with ADHD are illustrated in case studies of this book while options for assessment and treatment are explained in Chapters 14, 15, and 16 of this book.

Some, not all, of these very bright children, teens and adults also have a second problem—they tend to have difficulties in understanding and managing their emotions and may be awkward socially. Many have considerable difficulty in understanding other people, especially their age mates. Some tend to ignore or simply do not grasp social expectations readily followed by most others their age. Their cognitive intelligence is above average, but their social communication and emotional intelligence is more limited. For them, the social-emotional management system of the brain is impaired. These difficulties with social and emotional functioning are illustrated here in case studies while options for assessment and treatment are explained in Chapters 15 and 16 of this book.

A 10-Year-Old Boy with Both ADHD and Social-Emotional Impairment

The following clinical example illustrates one of the many ways in which this combination of ADHD and social-emotional impairments may be seen in childhood. Subsequent chapters offer examples of various ways in which this syndrome appears in other children, in adolescents and in adults.

Dan, a slender red-headed 10-year-old boy, came to our clinic with both of his parents, who suspected that he might have ADHD. They sought this consultation because, although extremely bright, Dan had been having a lot of academic and social difficulties in school. They reported that he did very well in subjects that especially interested him, particularly math or reading, but he was extremely slow or unable to complete assignments. He was also very easily distracted from most assigned tasks. They also reported that Dan was very shy, easily frustrated, and was teased and bullied by classmates so often that frequently he was unwilling or unable to go to school.

Dan was sitting on my office couch with his parents as I started our conversation by asking him to tell me his current grade in school and the name of his teacher. I heard him say fourth grade, but was not able to hear the name he said for his teacher. I responded: "Sorry, I didn't hear what you said your teacher's name is. Would you say it again please?"

Immediately Dan began sobbing. He stood up quickly, picking up a pillow off the couch. He held it above his head and angrily threw it to the floor. He then dropped to his knees and hid his face in the pillow while continuing his sobbing. His mother spoke: "Dan, you don't have to be so emotional. The doctor simply asked you to repeat the name of your teacher." Dan responded emphatically shouting, "I don't do emotions!"

Obviously, Dan did do emotions. In those moments, with much drama he displayed his frustration, his anger, and his embarrassment in response to my inability to understand when he tried to tell me the name of his teacher. Yet, in another sense, Dan was quite right. He was not able to "do" emotions in the sense of being able adequately to understand and process emotions involved in that brief interaction with me. He reacted as though I were angrily confronting him with an embarrassing mistake. He overreacted with a disproportionate meltdown.

After Dan was able to settle down a bit, he told me that such meltdowns were not unusual for him. They occurred frequently at home and at school. He explained that he felt unable to stop them and that other kids often called him "Baby Danny" because he was so easily upset and quick to cry. He said he liked to learn, except for writing, but he hated going to school because the kids were often mean to him. Quite articulately he explained that even in his earlier school years, "Usually the teachers liked me, except when I didn't get my work done, but I was always kind of an outsider. I had no friends, so I just kept to myself, stayed near the fence during recess, and read a lot of books. That's how it is now too."

In the course of our evaluation, it became very clear that Dan did, in fact, have ADHD. He, his parents and his teacher reported that he had chronic difficulty with many of the self-management functions characteristic of ADHD:

- He could focus extremely well on tasks that really interested him like math, but had chronic difficulty in focusing on and sustaining effort for tasks or activities that he found boring, like language arts, even when he knew it was important to get that work done.
- His teacher reported that he repeatedly seemed to drift off into his own thoughts, losing track of what was going on in the classroom.
- He was often quick to respond in class discussions, but was usually very slow to get started on assigned tasks and took much longer than classmates to complete assignments.
- He was frequently distracted by small noises or activities going on around him or out in the hall.
- He was often forgetful and had difficulty in remembering directions, even just moments after the teacher had explained them; he often needed to have directions repeated several times.
- When reading self-selected books he had good recollection of details from the story, but when reading something in which he was not interested, he consistently was unable to remember what he had read just a few moments earlier.

Dan also demonstrated many strengths. He was highly articulate with a precocious vocabulary. On IQ testing his verbal comprehension abilities and visual spatial abilities were higher than 99% of his age-mates. His scores for achievement in reading, spelling and math were stronger than for 98% of his peers. Yet, despite these outstanding strengths, Dan disliked school. On many mornings he stubbornly refused to leave home to go to school.

Dan gave two reasons for his reluctance to go to school. One was that he usually felt bored because he had already learned much of what was being covered in class; he claimed that often he knew more about the topic than what was being taught. Second, he dreaded going to school because often other kids said he was weird or called him Baby Dan, especially when he got upset and cried. He just wanted to be left alone so he could read and go on the internet.

When asked how his friends or classmates might describe him, Dan responded "smart in math," "reads a lot," "shy and quiet," "prefers to do things by himself," and "gets mad easily." His father described Dan as "often ironic with an adult sense of humor." Dan's mother noted that Dan "is often very impatient," "is extremely perfectionistic, and quick to tear up any picture he draws that is not perfect." She also mentioned that "almost always he seems weighted down."

After several hours of conversation, rating scales and some testing with Dan and his family, it became clear that this boy was suffering from the executive function impairments that constitute ADHD. However, ADHD was not his only problem. He was suffering also from that complex syndrome of social communication and interaction that often goes unrecognized and untreated. Dan's parents readily agreed with the ADHD diagnosis, but they were puzzled and worried when we began to talk about how Dan appeared also to have significant social-emotional impairment which, in our clinic, we refer to as Asperger syndrome. His mother interrupted, "Asperger syndrome? Isn't that part of autism? Dan's not autistic! He has excellent language skills and he's always been very affectionate with us. He's just a little shy!"

We assured his parents that Dan was not autistic in the classical sense. Most children diagnosed with classical autism are recognized before their third birthday to be severely impaired in basic social interaction. They tend to avoid eye contact and do not interact well with others by smiling or facial gestures; most are seriously delayed in developing language and are very limited intellectually, with IQ scores ranging from low average to severely disabled. None of those descriptions fit Dan.

A Useful Diagnosis that Disappeared

Once there was an official diagnosis to describe this puzzling combination of strong cognitive abilities with weak social-emotional functioning. In 1994 the American Psychiatric Association's *Diagnostic and Statistical Manual of Mental Disorders* provided the diagnosis of Asperger's Disorder for individuals such as the children, teens, and adults described in this book. Unfortunately, the most recent, 2013 edition of that manual (DSM-5) eliminated the Asperger diagnosis altogether (American Psychiatric Association, 2013). It stipulated that all those previously diagnosed as having Asperger's Syndrome should thereafter be diagnosed instead as simply being on the Autism Spectrum, a diagnosis previously used to describe only those with much more severe social and cognitive impairments. The most recent diagnostic manual of the World Health Organization, the International Classification of Diseases (ICD-11), also removed the Asperger diagnosis to merge it with the autism spectrum diagnosis (World Health Organization, 2018).

Elimination of the Asperger diagnosis has left individuals such as those described in this book without any official diagnosis to describe their unique combination of strengths and weaknesses. It has lumped them together with a group of children, teens and adults, most of whom have much more severe social impairments and much more limited intelligence. Bright individuals with social-emotional impairments need very different kinds of support and treatment than most others seen as on the autism spectrum.

Despite its elimination from the current version of the DSM and the ICD-11, our clinic for ADHD and related problems continues to use the term Asperger Syndrome for educational purposes when dealing with those patients and their families who are struggling with ADHD and this currently orphaned syndrome.

In some ways these smart, but socially and emotionally awkward individuals do resemble people with autism. They are significantly impaired in their social communications and interactions. They may have logical understanding of social situations, but they have much difficulty in understanding implied emotions of others. They tend to avoid or to be very slow in developing relationships with peers. They also tend to have a much more limited range of interests and activities than most others of similar age.

Yet in other ways, the people described in this book are quite different from most individuals considered autistic. Unlike the majority of those diagnosed with autism, their problems do not usually become apparent during infancy or early childhood. Usually they have not experienced significant delays in developing language skills and they do not suffer from below average cognitive abilities. To the contrary, those described in this book all have language and overall cognitive abilities solidly in the average range, many are in the high average or superior range. In addition, many are quite talented and or gifted in specific domains. Often their social impairments were not fully apparent until they entered elementary school where peer interaction is required or in middle school when they are challenged to function more independently with less consistent supervision from parents or other adults.

Lopsidedness in Understanding of the Autism Spectrum

The difficulty Dan's parents had in thinking about their son possibly having some traits of the autism spectrum is an example of a significant problem in current popular and professional understanding of autism. Current understanding of the autism spectrum is seriously lop-sided! Professional and advocacy groups have quite effectively worked for much needed recognition, treatment, educational and in-home support services for those on the spectrum who are most severely impaired, those whose intellectual abilities are extremely limited, those whose development of language is severely delayed. Meanwhile, there is much less recognition and extremely limited understanding, treatment, and support services for those on the smart end of the spectrum who in earlier days would have been diagnosed with Asperger syndrome.

Purposes of this book

This book extends my earlier book, *Smart but Stuck: Emotions in Teens and Adults with ADHD*, by expanding understanding of ADHD and its treatment while looking closely at case examples of 12 specific children, teens, and adults seen in our clinic who have suffered from significant social-emotional impairments while they also struggled with executive function impairments of ADHD. The book is intended not only for professionals in medicine and mental health, but also for educators and parents of smart children or teens who have ADHD with or without social-emotional impairments, and also for any adult who may have similar strengths and difficulties.

I have three purposes for writing this book:

1   To provide an updated, practical description of current science-based understanding of ADHD as a syndrome of developmental impairments in the brain's self-management system, its executive functions. This description goes beyond the official diagnostic criteria to illustrate in practical terms and examples what ADHD looks like in daily life of various children, teens, and adults. It also explains the "central mystery of ADHD," the fact that all who have ADHD are able to exercise these self-management functions reasonably well, sometimes very well, for a few specific tasks or activities in which they have strong interest, even though for most other activities they experience much difficulty. In addition, this book offers descriptions of how ADHD impairments can be recognized and effectively treated.

2   To describe and explain the syndrome previously known as Asperger Syndrome, now eliminated from the diagnostic manual. This syndrome, found in children, teens, and adults, is a unique combination of solidly average or above average cognitive abilities in individuals who also demonstrate significantly impaired social-emotional functioning that, in some ways, appears quite similar to a type of autism. At the same time, those affected with this syndrome are very different from most others on the autism spectrum because of their much better developed language abilities and their significantly stronger cognitive intelligence. They are also quite different from one another. This book offers a variety of specific examples of different strategies, techniques and medications that may be helpful in recognizing and supporting individuals with Asperger Syndrome and ADHD in their efforts to cope adaptively with specific social-emotional challenges at various stages of life.

3   To advocate for restoring use of the term "Asperger Syndrome" to iden-
     tify those on the autism spectrum with stronger cognitive abilities so they
     can be provided adequate help to develop their potential for social inter-
     action which is stronger than most others on the autistic spectrum. Just as
     in psychiatric diagnosis there is good reason to differentiate "Separation
     Anxiety" from "Specific Phobia," "Social Anxiety," "Panic Disorder" and
     "Generalized Anxiety Disorder" rather than lumping them altogether
     simply as "Anxiety Disorders," it is also useful to identify Asperger Syn-
     drome as a cluster of characteristics that is different from other types on
     the Autism Spectrum, and to recognize the need for those with this syn-
     drome to be helped to prepare for more complex social interactions. I
     urge the American Psychiatric Association and the World Health Orga-
     nization to restore diagnostic criteria for Asperger Syndrome as a subset
     of Autism Spectrum Disorder.

Those on the autism spectrum whose cognitive abilities are in the average
or above average IQ range are expected gradually to function much more
independently in school and other complex social settings than are those on
the spectrum whose cognitive abilities are significantly more limited. Those on
the spectrum with these stronger cognitive abilities are less likely to be pro-
tected in self-contained classrooms at school and much more likely to be
interacting with mainstream peers in classrooms and, eventually, in employment and other settings where their social-emotional impairments are likely to
become more problematic.

This book begins with a chapter describing four successful adults who suffered from social-emotional impairments which were not recognized until they
were in their middle adult years. That chapter includes excerpts from their
biographical writings which reveal how their unrecognized social-emotional
impairments made life quite difficult for them during childhood and into their
adult years. Their writings also show how belated recognition of their social-
emotional impairments paved the way for them to make significant life-alter-
ing changes. Their writings also suggest that they may have suffered from
undiagnosed ADHD.

Following are twelve chapters rich with details about a variety of particular
children, teens and adults seen and diagnosed in our clinic who are quite
smart while they also suffered from social-emotional impairments we describe
as Asperger syndrome in addition to their having ADHD. Each case example
concludes with reflections on specific factors that helped or hindered that
person's functioning. I have carefully modified identifying information to
protect their privacy. Some of these individuals eventually became quite successful in various ways and others are still very much in process.

Following the 12 case examples, Chapter 14 describes our science-based
understanding of ADHD while Chapter 15 describes Asperger syndrome and
explains why we use that term and not "Asperger's syndrome" to refer to
social-emotional impairments in these very bright individuals.

Chapter 16 describes how ADHD and Asperger syndrome are not mutually exclusive diagnostic "silos," but often co-occur in many individuals. That chapter also illustrates how both Asperger syndrome and ADHD are often accompanied by some or many features of learning problems, emotional syndromes or behavioral difficulties.

The book concludes with Chapter 17 that summarizes resources, strategies, and medications we have found useful in providing help for smart children, teenagers and adults who have ADHD with the social-emotional impairments of Asperger syndrome as they struggle to cope with their difficulties and to develop their impressive strengths.

Following Chapter 17 is a listing of references and resources utilized or referred to in this book. The first section includes references for articles and books that may be helpful for teens or adults with ADHD and/or Asperger syndrome, their parents or caretakers, as well as for educators or clinicians providing services for those with ADHD, Asperger syndrome, or both.

The second section includes additional references utilized in the book and some more specialized references that may be of interest to clinicians, academics, and researchers.

Part I
Starting Points and Potential Destinations

1 Smart Adults with Late-Recognized Asperger Syndrome and Success

In this chapter are excerpts from autobiographical writings by four very successful adults with social-emotional impairments (Asperger syndrome), which offer examples of their strengths and difficulties. Although none of these four writers was identified previous to their adult years as having ADHD, each includes in their writings clear examples of difficulties that make it likely that they have had ADHD as well as Asperger syndrome.

One autobiographical description of growing up smart with Asperger syndrome has been provided by **Tim Page** who, despite dropping out of school after seventh grade, became a Pulitzer Prize-winning writer who eventually served as chief music critic for the *Washington Post*. He is currently a professor of journalism at the University of Southern California. In his *Parallel Play: Growing Up with Undiagnosed Aspergers*, Page wrote of his difficulties interacting with peers:

> my life has been spent in a perpetual state of parallel play, alongside, but distinctly apart from the rest of humanity … I could establish no connection with most of my classmates … [later] I learned that there were others like me—people who yearned for steady routines, repeated patterns … and a few cherished subjects.
>
> (Page, 2009, pp. 3–5)

In spite of scoring in the top 2% for his age on an IQ test, in his earlier school years Page had chronic difficulty in sustaining attention and focus for most of his schoolwork. He reported that

> If I wasn't deeply interested in a subject, I couldn't concentrate on it at all … Late in each quarter, when it became obvious to me that I had no clue to what I was supposed to have learned, I'd attend some makeup sessions and try desperately to pay attention … My grades only worsened as teachers expected more of me … The school was perplexed by my behavior, for it was increasingly obvious that I was not "normal" … I lagged

DOI: 10.4324/9781003141976-3

consistently at or near that bottom of the class, decidedly out of control—either asleep or aggressively assertive—much of the time. Grade seven was the last one I was able to complete.

(Page, 2009, pp. 37, 38, 56)

Yet despite his continuing difficulty with most of his schoolwork, Page demonstrated extraordinary talents in some fields which held great interest for him. "I took to the piano naturally and joyfully, and was composing before I formally knew how" (Page, 2009, p. 39). He felt repulsed by popular music of those days, but he read all the opera books in the local university library and became fully familiar with classical and contemporary music as well as the history of silent film. During his early teens Page also developed interest in making home movies, one of which gained some recognition on a national level.

In his mid to late teens, Page found some friends who shared his interest in music. With them he became increasingly involved in a protracted period of excessive drinking and using marijuana. During that time he also experienced episodes of acute anxiety and deep depression. This exacerbated after he was involved in a tragic motor vehicle accident in which two of his friends were killed. In his late teens Page resumed his education and eventually graduated from Columbia University

It was not until midlife that Page learned that he had Asperger syndrome. He wrote of the surprise and relief he felt when he first received that diagnosis and read a book that described it:

> I felt as though I had stumbled upon my secret biography. Here it all was—the computer-like retention, the physical awkwardness, the difficulties with peers and lovers, the need for routine and repetition, the narrow, specialized interests—I was forty-five years old when I learned that I wasn't alone.
>
> (Page, 2009, p.178)

Another autobiographical account was provided by **Temple Grandin** in her book *Thinking in Pictures: My Life with Autism*. Grandin describes herself as having the symptoms of classic autism when she was two years old: no speech, poor eye contact, tantrums, appearance of deafness, no interest in people, and constantly staring off into space. Yet, she noted that as an adult she would probably be diagnosed as having Asperger Syndrome (Grandin, 2006, p. 49). She provides a good example of how level of impairment in persons with autistic characteristics can improve considerably over the course of development.

Grandin described high school as "the worst time of my life ... High functioning teenagers on the spectrum often get bullied in high school ... I was kicked out of a large girls' high school after I threw a book at a girl who teased me" (Grandin, 2006, p. 120). In her autobiography Grandin notes the role of her mother and various teachers and other mentors in helping her develop her impressive potential:

> It was Mr. Carlock, one of my science teachers, who became my most important mentor in high school. After I was thrown out of regular high school, my

parents enrolled me in a small boarding school for gifted students with emotional problems. Even though I scored 137 (99th percentile) on the Wechsler IQ test when I was twelve, I was totally bored with schoolwork and I continued to get lousy grades ... but Mr. Carlock took my interests as motivators for doing schoolwork ... I have observed that high-functioning autistic individuals who become successful have two important factors in their lives: mentoring and the development of talents.

(Grandin, 2006, pp. 104, 116)

When she arrived at Arizona State University, Grandin struggled to learn the rules and expectations in the university community. "College was a confusing place, and I strove to use visual analogies to understand the rules of collegiate society."

For people with autism, rules are very important, because we concentrate intensely on how things are done ... Since I don't have any social intuition, I rely on pure logic, like an expert computer program, to guide my behavior. It is a complex algorithmic decision- making tree. There is a process of using my intellect and logical decision-making for every social decision. Emotion does not guide my decision; it is pure computing.

(Grandin, 2006, p. 108)

Ultimately, Grandin was quite successful at Arizona State University; she went on to earn a bachelor's degree in psychology and a master's degree in animal science. Her specialty was studying the behavior of cattle in feedlots as they were put through various types of cattle chutes. She designed widely used equipment to manage them more humanely. Despite her occupational success, Grandin struggled with increasing anxiety, often accompanied by bouts of colitis or severe headaches. She wrote that her nervous system was constantly under stress. "I was like a frightened animal, and every little thing triggered a fear reaction ... In my late twenties, these severe attacks became more and more frequent" (Grandin, 2006, p. 124). In 1981 Grandin found medication that helped to alleviate her chronic anxiety.

My body was no longer in a state of hyperarousal. Before taking the drug, I had been in a constant state of physiological alertness, as if ready to flee a non-existent predator ... Taking the medication is like adjusting the idle adjustment screw on an old-fashioned automobile engine. Before I took it, my engine was racing all the time, doing so many revolutions per minute that it was tearing itself up. Now my nervous system is running at 55 mph instead of 200 mph, as it used to ... about half of high functioning autistic adults have severe anxiety and panic ... Today there are many new drug treatments can be really helpful to people with autism ... Unfortunately, many medical professionals do not know how to prescribe them properly ... people with autism often require lower doses of anti-depressants than nonautistic people.

(Grandin, 2006, pp. 126, 128, 130)

A third autobiographical account of growing up smart with Asperger syndrome comes from **Cynthia Kim**, author of *Nerdy, Shy and Socially Inappropriate: A User Guide to an Asperger Life*. She reports that she did not know she had Asperger syndrome until she was 40 years old. She came to know about this syndrome from hearing a radio program about it. As she listened, she recognized aspects of herself which, despite her successes, had been problematic for her since childhood.

> I grew up in an era when my diagnosis—Asperger's syndrome—didn't yet exist. Kids like me were labeled nerdy, shy, or gifted. Year after year I brought home report cards that said I didn't work and play well with others, didn't participate in class. Because I was quiet and did well academically, the adults in my life attributed my difficulties to extreme shyness and timidity … [now] on the face of it, I'm a typical suburban middle-aged woman. I'm happily married, a successful small business owner, and proud mom of a terrific young woman … [yet] I have all of the telltale signs of Asperger's: poor social skills, communication difficulties, sensory sensitivities, a deep love of routines, lots of subtle stims, the working memory of a goldfish … the list is long and varied.
>
> (Kim, 2015, pp. 13–14)

Kim describes her growing up as a time of considerable social isolation:

> I was definitely different from my peers. For one thing, I spent hours alone. Some of my happiest memories are of long bike rides around my rural neighborhood, exploring in the woods, and playing games in my room, all by myself. I remember quite a few fiercely contested games of Risk and Monopoly that pitted me against myself …
>
> She's just shy! I heard that phrase over and over again. If I didn't participate in discussions in school, it was because I was shy. If I sat on the sidelines at a birthday party or went off to read in an empty bedroom, it was because I was shy. If I didn't want to be in the school play or I didn't have many friends—all part of my shyness. I was a good girl. I didn't make waves.
>
> (Kim, 2015, pp. 20–23)

However, Kim also described herself as repeatedly teased or bullied in elementary school. She reported that she often felt like an antelope surrounded by a pack of hungry lions coming to attack her:

> When you're a kid who has little idea how social group dynamics work, it's easy to feel like the whole world is out to get you. For years I put up with the bullying because I didn't know how to stop it.
>
> One day, when one of the mean girls in the neighborhood said something nasty to me, I said something nasty right back … And it worked … After a few nasty exchanges we became something like friends … I found frenemies—

developing relationships with other girls that thrived on getting along one day and cutting each other to shreds with insults the next. Soon all my friends were other mean girls … When we got bored with harassing each other, we went looking for easy targets … kids who were loners and outcasts. Kids who stand out because of their looks. Kids who don't have allies to defend them. It's easy to spot a victim when you've been one yourself.

(Kim, 2015, p. 27)

In describing her years in elementary school, Kim observes:

For kids who are developmentally disabled but intellectually gifted, expecting them to get by on intelligence alone is the equivalent of throwing them in the deep end of the pool without teaching them to swim first. It's leaving them to drown—emotionally and mentally—all the while telling them how smart they are.

(Kim, 2015, p. 32)

Kim reported that in high school she found interests she could pursue together with people who did not tease or bully her:

The other mean girls drifted away one by one. I had fewer friends, just one close friend, but I wasn't so afraid. I no longer needed to wrap myself in the armor of bullying to get through the school day or walk through my neighborhood.

(Kim, 2015, p. 28)

However, her difficulties did not end in high school:

When you arrive in adulthood lacking the social skills that most people have mastered by sixth grade, life becomes exponentially more confusing and hard to navigate … Typical people acquire social skills mainly by absorption … we need to be taught social skills explicitly. When we're not, we're no more likely to learn them instinctively than we are to intuitively pick up algebra … Where other adults seem to rely on gut reactions and intuitive responses, I rely on a catalog of past experiences for navigating social interactions.

(Kim, 2015, pp. 32–34)

A fourth autobiographical account of growing up smart with Asperger syndrome comes from **John Robison**, author of the bestseller, *Look Me in the Eye: My Life with Asperger's*. In that book he described how he felt and acted very different from other kids his age as he was growing up:

I was different from other kids … I walked with a mechanical, robotic gait. I moved clumsily. My facial expressions were rigid and I seldom smiled. Often I failed to respond to other people at all. I acted as though they weren't even there. Most of the time I stayed alone, in my own little world, apart from my peers ... When I did interact with other kids, the interactions were usually awkward. I seldom met anyone's gaze.

(Robison, 2008, p. 4)

Robison was very bright, scoring at the 99th percentile on an IQ test, but he dropped out of high school at 15 years old when he was in the 10th grade. He left school because he was consistently ridiculed and harassed for being socially awkward; and he was failing academically. Despite this, he gradually developed his skills in technology. He repaired sound equipment for musicians and eventually became quite successful as an engineer. In the late 1970s he worked as technician and manager of the sound and lighting systems for the very successful rock band Kiss. Later he was employed as a staff engineer for electronics in a manufacturing company where he developed his ability to solve complex technical and mathematical problems, but he ran into difficulties due to his limited interpersonal skills. He described this in his autobiography:

The trouble was, the higher I advanced in the corporate world, the more I had to rely on my people skills and the less my technical skills and creativity mattered ... By 1988 I had moved through two more corporate jobs, and I had swallowed all I could take of the corporate world. I had come to accept what my performance reviews said, I was not a team player. I had trouble communicating with people ... I was smart and creative, yes, but I was a misfit.

(Robison, 2008, pp. 204–205)

This frustration led Robison to open up his own car repair shop where he specialized in working on high-end vehicles like Rolls-Royces and Land Rovers:

I loved the way they were put together ... I had found a niche where many of my Aspergian traits actually benefitted me. My compulsion to know everything about cars made me a great service person. My precise speech gave me the ability to explain complex problems in simple terms. My directness meant I told people what they needed to know about their cars ...

(Robison, 2008, p. 214)

Yet Robison quickly recognized that developing a successful car repair business required more than just his skills in diagnosing and repairing cars.

Before going into the business of fixing cars, I had always looked at car repair as fundamentally simpler than, say engineering. Having now done both, I know that isn't true. If anything, running an automotive repair business is harder for me because it uses a different kind of brainpower— a kind I had never developed during my engineering days. I had to acquire a broad range of new skills, and fast. Chief among them was the ability to deal with people in a friendly way that would make them want to return.

(Robison, 2008, pp. 214–215)

In concluding his autobiography Robison emphasized that he had gradually developed more skills in interacting with others.

My life today is immeasurably happier, richer and fuller as a result of my brain's continuing development … Many descriptions of autism and Asperger's describe people like me as "not wanting contact with others" or "preferring to play alone." I can't speak for other kids … but I did not ever want to be alone … I played by myself because I was a failure at playing with others. I was alone as a result of my own limitations, and being alone was one of the bitterest disappointments of my young life … I hope this book demonstrates that however robotic we Aspergians might seem, we do have deep feelings.

(Robison, 2008, p. 211)

Part II
Children and Teenagers

2   Joshua

> I'm in school to work ahead and get to college faster where I can be around others who are very smart like I am and who will share my interests in music and theoretical physics. I don't have friends at this school. I'm lonely there; the other kids aren't like me. But at least I'm not getting bullied like I was in my last school. I used to be pretty depressed and had thoughts of suicide, but that's been better recently. I still worry a lot though about whether I'll meet my goal to skip ahead to a higher grade.

Joshua came with his mother for an initial consultation with me when he was 11 years old and enrolled in fifth grade at a very small private school where each student was in a separate cubicle to work at his own pace with little social interaction between students. This school setting was a welcome refuge for Joshua after three years in a public school where he was frequently shunned and bullied by other students. Joshua began by describing himself breathlessly:

> I'm a nerd who is in school to work ahead. I get along better with grownups and older kids than with kids my age. I don't have any friends at school. I'm lonely there. I want to get into high school as soon as possible and then get into college where I'll be with other people who are very smart like I am. When I get there I want to major in theoretical physics and minor in law or business. I've always had trouble focusing on anything for long. And I've always had depression and sometimes thoughts of suicide. I also have migraines and am germ phobic. I wash my hands until they're red and raw. I also fidget a lot with my feet.

Two years prior to his evaluation in our clinic, while he was in third grade in a mainstream public school, Joshua was referred by his parents for a neuropsychological evaluation. At that time he was seen as an extremely bright student who was struggling with sensory sensitivities, migraine headaches, difficulties in sustaining attention in school, and problems in getting along with other students.

On a sentence completion task in that evaluation Joshua stated "Other kids … are mean to me and annoy me. I can't understand why … kids are so mean to me." He stated "my mother thinks … I am very nice and special," and "My father thinks I … am very nice and special." When asked what three wishes he

DOI: 10.4324/9781003141976-5

would want granted, he stated, "I wish for everybody to be nicer to me, that I would be able to fly, and to be able to do anything." In these sentence responses Joshua appeared clueless as to why other kids picked on him and were mean to him. Meanwhile, he perceived himself as "very nice and special" in the eyes of both parents. He also was wishing for everybody to be nicer to him, to be able soar above others, and to have unlimited powers.

On the Social Responsiveness Scale-2 (Constantino and Gruber, 2012), a measure of reciprocal social function and autism-related characteristics we used in our assessment, Joshua's parents rated him as having only mild social impairments. In contrast, all three of his teachers independently rated Joshua as having severe impairments in social awareness, social communication, social cognition, restricted and repetitive behaviors, and social motivation. Joshua's parents seemed unaware of the severity of their son's social impairments. They supported him in his view of himself as a faultless victim of peer hostilities while communicating to him that he was "very nice and special." Such discrepancies between parental understanding of their child and views of the child by school staff are especially likely in families with an only child and parents who have never experienced sibling competition for parental attention and praise.

Joshua felt special because his parents repeatedly praised him for being "gifted" and highly intelligent, much smarter than other children. Yet, from his teachers and his peers Joshua was given a different message—that he was not so competent in activities considered important in the classroom or playground. That more negative message was not effectively countered by his parents' efforts to tell him that other children teased him simply because they were jealous of his impressive intelligence and abilities. He struggled with feelings of inadequacy in dealing with classmates and felt increasingly demoralized by his lack of positive connections with other children his age.

There is considerable social risk for children who are excessively praised by their parents for being exceptionally intelligent. First, they are likely to develop a sense of superiority over others their age while not developing appropriate respect and appreciation for the different strengths of others. Resulting attitudes of condescension are readily picked up by classmates, some of whom are likely to respond by pointing out areas of weakness in the one who sees himself as the king of the hill.

Second, when children are repeatedly praised for their intelligence, they are likely to give up too quickly when they encounter tasks they cannot readily master. They may assume that they are not so intelligent after all. A number of studies have demonstrated that when children are praised for their intelligence rather than for their efforts, their self-confidence tends to be more fragile. Psychologist Carol Dweck and colleagues have shown that

> when parents respond to their children's success by acknowledging their hard work, … reminding them that what is important is not their actual grades but how hard they are trying … that will usually enhance their learning … and increase their persistence when tasks are frustrating.
>
> (Pomerantz, Grolnick, and Price, 2005, p. 264)

When Joshua was evaluated in our clinic there was substantial evidence of his being very intelligent. On the WISC-V IQ test his scores for verbal comprehension and for fluid reasoning were stronger than 98–99 percent of his age mates. However, his score for processing speed was in the low average range, worse than 91% of his peers. Our research has demonstrated that many high IQ adolescents and adults with ADHD tend to score relatively low on measures of working memory and/or processing speed despite their very strong scores for verbal and visual spatial measures (Brown, Reichel, and Quinlan, 2009, 2011b).

My evaluation of Joshua clearly indicated that he fully met diagnostic criteria for ADHD of the combined type. Clinical interviews with Joshua and his parents brought multiple examples of Joshua's ability to focus very well on tasks which strongly interested him while he had much chronic difficulty in sustaining focus and effort for tasks which were not personally interesting to him or which he could not quickly master. Rating scale responses from Joshua, his parents and his current teacher all placed him in the "very significant problem" range on the Brown Executive Function/Attention Rating Scale (Brown, 2019) which assesses for executive skills needed to sustain motivation and effort for tasks which the individual does not see as especially interesting.

Like the psychologist who had evaluated him years earlier, I found that in addition to being very bright and having ADHD, Joshua also suffered from chronic anxiety with some obsessive compulsive features. The previous psychologist had also noted that "while he may not fully meet criteria for Autism Spectrum Disorder, he demonstrates multiple autistic traits." My impression of Joshua's impairments in social functioning was similar. I told him and his parents that I thought of him as meeting criteria for Asperger syndrome, taught them what that means, and suggested that we target those symptoms as well as his ADHD and anxiety as targets for ongoing treatment.

One major area of strength where Joshua's ADHD impairments were not evident was making music. Early in his childhood he had demonstrated much interest and rapid development of skill for playing piano. In that domain he did not brag about his skills because in recitals and concerts he was readily exposed to others, some his own age and many much older, who were obviously more proficient in playing piano than he was. Yet he enjoyed practicing and gradually mastering new pieces in both classical music and jazz suggested by his music teacher.

Joshua's mother was very aware of the limitations of the small private school Joshua had been attending. She recognized how in that setting he was getting no adequate opportunities for learning how to improve his impaired skills in social interaction. Yet she also knew that he would be likely to struggle if he entered a conventional public or private middle school, given his recent painful experiences with being shunned and bullied by classmates.

After making multiple inquiries Joshua's mother located a charter magnet school for students with interests and talent in various arts. Admission was competitive by audition in the particular domain where the student had demonstrated ability. The school was a considerable distance from their home, but transportation service was available for students with a long commute. She took Joshua for a tour of the school where he saw many talented students who shared his strong interest in music as well as many others with interests and talent in dance, theater or visual arts. He found the school very appealing and agreed to prepare for an audition to seek admission.

Joshua performed very well at his audition and was accepted into the school's music program. He began there a few months later. Not surprisingly, as the time to begin in the new school approached, Joshua became increasingly anxious and fearful that he would not be able to fit in, despite his sharing very similar interests with students in the division of the school he was entering.

In his first therapy session after starting in the new school Joshua told his parents and me about an incident on his hour-long van ride to the school with nine other students. As Joshua squeezed into the back of the crowded van, an African American boy teasingly commented "You're a little pudgy, can you fit in back there?" Impulsively Joshua responded, "Well, at least I'm not black!" Joshua realized his mistake immediately and blurted out an apology. Joshua then remained quiet while none of the other students spoke to him for the rest of the long ride.

After some coaching during his psychotherapy session Joshua agreed to approach the boy he had offended in the van. On the next school day he simply told him, "Sorry about what I said yesterday. I'm not really racist, I was just really uptight about my first day at the school." Fortunately, the boy responded by saying "No problem, I remember how I felt my first day. You'll get used to how we 'roast' each other once in a while, but we can still be friends."

Despite that awkward first day, Joshua gradually settled into his new school. He quickly adjusted to the academic portion of the curriculum which was challenging, but manageable for him. Social adjustment was more difficult. His teachers reported to Joshua's parents that he was participating fully in classes and that he was interacting with other students during class, but was still too fearful to interact with other students in unstructured situations. For several weeks he avoided the cafeteria and ate his sack lunch alone in a more isolated area of campus.

Joshua reported that he often had difficulty in understanding what the other kids were talking about when they were outside the classrooms. He felt especially uncomfortable around the many girls and some gay boys who were hanging around them. He noted:

> they're always gossiping and looking at Instagram together. I can't understand much of what they're talking about. It's like that Calvin and Hobbes cartoon saying "We're both speaking English, but we're not speaking the same language."

With this observation Joshua highlighted a problem often experienced by adolescents with Asperger syndrome who have spent relatively little time with peers and have not become familiar with the contemporary subculture and patterns of informal communication among their age group. Not only do they have difficulty in picking up sarcasm and the significance of non-verbal communications; often they also are not at all familiar with many of the people, topics and interests being discussed or referred to. Joshua reported that one day a girl invited him to join her and her friends at lunch. He accepted, but reported that he didn't know what to say. "I felt so shy and so scared that I would come across as a weird foreigner."

It is hard to overestimate the impact of peer interactions in shaping an individual's patterns of interacting with others. Judith Harris has written about how the role of parents in shaping an individual's social skills is much less powerful than is usually assumed (Harris, 1998, 2006). She reviews evidence from research that demonstrates how peer interactions are usually much more powerful in shaping social attitudes and behavior than are parental behaviors and examples.

After he had been in the new school for a couple of months Joshua told me that the other kids in his school "are not talented in every way, each one is just talented in a particular way. They're just like normal kids." This recognition was an important step for him in recognizing that others in his classes, like himself, were not totally superior, that they were very talented in particular domains where they had special talents and worked hard. This paved the way for him to begin recognizing his own mix of weaknesses and strengths.

In our therapy session one week later Joshua proudly reported that he had been selected to perform in a special jazz group at his school. He also reported that he had gotten himself in an awkward situation by talking with much contempt about "commercial music," a term he used to describe popular music that was a primary focus for several students in the vocal music program at his school who were in his English class. They had heatedly pointed out that their music was fully as respectable as the jazz or classical music preferred by Joshua. This is just one of many situations where Joshua needed help to learn the importance of showing respect for interests and competence of others whose strengths are in different fields. Gradually he began to understand and utilize such social skills for dealing with peers, skills he had for interacting with adults, but did not pick up in his earlier years.

In addition to individual and conjoint family psychotherapy, we used medication to support Joshua with his intense social anxiety and his ADHD-related executive function impairments. This was necessary to protect his sleep, to alleviate anxiety that was causing episodes of vomiting before or after school, and to alleviate his ADHD impairments that were interfering with his academic work.

Prior to his treatment at our clinic Joshua had been tried on Concerta and guanfacine for his ADHD, and on three different SSRI medications (fluoxetine, sertraline, and citalopram) to reduce his anxiety and improve his depressed mood. Joshua and his parents reported that all of those medications caused adverse effects which he could not tolerate; they had to be discontinued.

Given his sensitive body chemistry, we decided to try a minimal dose of Vyvanse for his ADHD, just 10 mg, which he was able to tolerate. This was later increased to 20 mg and then to 30 mg which he found quite helpful and tolerable. Once that was stabilized, we did a trial of buproprion-XL to reduce his anxiety and improve his mood. That medication had been helpful to several closely related members of his family. He started with one tab of 150 mg XL, which proved helpful for reducing his anxiety and also improved his mood. When he complained of that the Vyvanse was wearing off in mid-afternoon it was increased to 1 tab in the morning and a second, lower dose in mid-afternoon. He also was given a 0.25 dose of clonazepam that he could use occasionally as needed at bedtime if he had excessive difficulty getting to sleep.

Reflections on Joshua and Beyond

Our experience with children, teens, and adults who have Asperger syndrome has taught us that many of them have a very sensitive body chemistry which requires starting any medication at very small doses, careful monitoring, and slow increase or adjustments of dose to match their needs and response. For many, including Joshua, the medication plays a very important role in helping to reduce their anxiety and to improve their functioning. Yet there is no one medication or combination of medications that works for all.

Joshua was impaired by rejection and hostility of his peers, but much of that rejection and hostility was reactive to his mode of interaction with them, his tendency to see himself as much smarter than his classmates, being condescending, not demonstrating appropriate respect and appreciation for the different strengths of others. These difficulties with peers were exacerbated by his parents emphasizing his being very smart and interpreting the peer criticism as simple jealousy rather than as, in part, a reaction to his condescension.

Joshua's functioning with peers was also exacerbated by his lack of sufficient contact with his age mates. Social expectations for interacting with peers are quite different from social expectations for interacting with adults or with age mates while they are supervised by adults. Children whose interactions with age mates outside their own household are excessively limited are deprived of needed opportunities to learn from observing and interacting with their peers where they can pick up understanding of peers that is not likely to be accurately provided by adults.

Especially as they get into later elementary school years, children learn by observing their peers and interactions of older children where they can see how the unwritten rules for what one says and does with peers are quite different when the adults are not around than when adults are present. They learn how to understand the shifting alliances and power relationships within the peer groups. If a child has insufficient opportunity to observe, learn to interpret and share in the shifting dynamics of interaction among their peers, they are likely to operate like a foreigner in an unknown culture.

Joshua's functioning was also impaired by earlier attempts to provide medication treatment for his ADHD without taking adequately into account the sensitivity of his body to those medications. Many children and adults with

Asperger syndrome have an exceptionally sensitive body chemistry, which makes it especially important to "fine-tune" medications they are given. It is not uncommon for those with Asperger syndrome to report that they have been tried on many different medications, none of which was helpful and most of which caused significant adverse effects. Evaluating clinicians should always get specific information about previous medications used, the specific doses prescribed, what benefits or adverse effects occurred, and approximately what time of day the adverse effects were noticed.

The issue of time of day an adverse side effect occurs can be helpful determining whether the unpleasant effects occurred during the day when the medication was active or later in the day as the medication was wearing off, possibly a rebound which might be easily avoided by adjusting timing of the dose or adding a small "booster dose" shortly before the time of day when the adverse effect usually occurred.

One important way in which Joshua's parents helped him was to remove him from the school placement where he was being consistently shunned and bullied throughout his third and fourth grade years, despite parental efforts to get teachers and school administrators to control those problematic harassments. Moving him to a private school where most instruction was done on a one-to-one basis provided a respite from those peer pressures, but it would not have been helpful over a longer term because it denied Joshua opportunity to participate in group instruction and projects with peers where he could develop his very limited social skills.

After considerable searching, Joshua's parents located the charter magnet school where their son auditioned and was accepted. Because that school was specifically designed for students with interest and talents in the arts, it provided an excellent opportunity for Joshua to learn in a setting where he could develop his special talents in music and where he would associate daily with other students who shared his strong musical interests. It turned out to be well worth the one-hour trip he had to make to and from school each day. It can be especially helpful for a student with Asperger syndrome to have frequent contact with peers with whom they can share a strong mutual interest.

Another way in which Joshua's parents helped him was providing him ongoing psychotherapy to coach him as he was making the transition into his new school. He did not need weekly sessions on an ongoing basis, but for his first few months at the new school it was helpful for us to have weekly sessions in which I could talk with Joshua and also use part of the time to talk with Joshua and his parents together about things like the incident with the boy in the van and the difficulties Joshua experienced in dealing with his social anxiety that kept him from joining other students for lunch during his first few weeks at the new school. After several months of weekly sessions we continued Joshua's psychotherapy on a twice-monthly basis and then gradually tapered it down to once per month, with the option to increase frequency if needed.

3 Sam

Our son with ADHD is doing OK in his schoolwork, but he gets teased a lot and makes trouble for himself by being too critical of other kids. Despite what we tell him, he can't keep his opinions to himself. He's always quick to point out when another kid makes a mistake, not only during classes, but also in practices and games with his baseball and basketball teams. He starts middle school in two months. We're really concerned about how he'll get along socially.

About two months before Sam was to start sixth grade in middle school his parents brought him for consultation in our clinic. He was a bright boy who had scored in the high average range on an IQ test several years earlier. Two years prior to this consultation Sam had been diagnosed with ADHD; he had been taking extended-release Focalin since that time. Sam and his parents reported that the medication had been quite helpful in reducing his hyperactivity in school and in improving his ability to pay attention and complete his work in class. However, soon after school ended each day, Sam became much more "hyper" than when he was not taking any medicine and he struggled to complete his homework. The parents did not want to give him more medicine after school because they feared it would curtail his appetite for dinner and make it difficult for him to fall asleep at night. They also worried that taking more medicine at this age might increase the likelihood of his developing an alcohol or drug dependence problem when he hit adolescence.

Sam's parents had two primary concerns in our first meeting. First, they wanted suggestions about how to reduce Sam's intensified restlessness and hyperactivity in late afternoon and early evening after the medicine had worn off. Their second concern was that Sam might encounter social problems with the older kids in middle school as he did when playing on his basketball and baseball teams.

The medication problem was not difficult. His parents had not been told about "rebound," a problem that occurs with some children and adults who take stimulant medications for ADHD. I explained that if someone taking a stimulant has difficulty with feeling very restless, very irritable, too tired, or too serious during the time the medication is active and then those difficulties diminish later in the day as the medication wears off, that usually indicates that the stimulant

DOI: 10.4324/9781003141976-6

dose is too high for that person or that the medication is not effective for their body chemistry. Usually the remedy is to reduce the dose; if that doesn't clear the problem it will probably be necessary to switch to a different medication. However, if those problems of excessive restlessness, irritability, seriousness or fatigue do not occur during the time the medication is active, but they do emerge as the medication is wearing off, that is a very different problem. It is not that the dose is too high; that would be seen during the time the medication is active.

Those symptoms of restlessness, irritability or excessive seriousness, lack of spontaneity or blunting of emotions, occurring only as the medication is wearing off are usually indications of a "rebound." Rebound usually means not that the dose of medication is too high, that would have been apparent during the time the medication is active. Rebound usually occurs when the dose is wearing off too fast so the person is "crashing." Usually rebound can be remedied with administration of a small dose of short-acting stimulant medication shortly before the "crash" occurs. If carefully fine-tuned, that booster dose usually provides a less abrupt drop-off of the medication, a smoother landing.

Often careful timing and fine-tuning is necessary to avoid problems with diminished appetite at dinner or problems in getting to sleep as well as to provide coverage for homework or other tasks that may need to be done in early evening. However, for some children, teens, or adults, the so-called long-acting stimulant may lose its effectiveness very early in the afternoon. In that situation it may be necessary to utilize a smaller dose of the long-acting stimulant as a booster in early afternoon to prevent rebound and to provide sufficient coverage for late afternoon and early evening. It turned out that Sam needed a longer-acting booster because he was a fast metabolizer of his stimulant medication.

As we discussed the medication Sam's parents spoke about their fear that their son's taking medication, especially more than one dose per day, might make him more vulnerable to developing a drug dependency problem during adolescence. I explained to them that there is good evidence that a child or adolescent with ADHD has twice the risk of developing a substance use disorder if they are not treated with medication for their ADHD. I told them that taking medication for ADHD does not guarantee that the child or teen will never develop a substance dependence disorder, but generally it does reduce the risk to what it would be for any child or teen who did not have ADHD (see Brown, 2017, pp. 199–200).

The second concern of Sam's parents was more difficult. They were worried about how he would adjust socially when he entered middle school where there would be many new kids, some of whom would be a year or two older. This was a concern because, though Sam had a couple of friends in his class, he didn't seem to fit in comfortably with most of the other boys. I asked Sam if kids were sometimes mean to him at school. He said that sometimes the boys would not make any room for him to sit at a lunch table where two of his friends were eating with other kids who did not like Sam. They would tell him that they were saving the only vacant seat for someone else, though usually no one else came while Sam had to sit at a table with the girls.

Sam also told how one boy would sometimes walk beside him in the hall and quietly say "You're so smart! I worship the ground you walk on!" The boy then walked away saying "You're such a loser!" I asked Sam if he had any idea about why those kids were mean to him. He said he didn't know, but that it could be that they were jealous because he was better at answering questions in class than they were.

There was not enough time in our initial consultation session to explore these social issues adequately so I asked Sam and his parents to try to think of some more examples of problems with other kids so that in our next session we could try to learn more about what the difficulties were and how Sam could find some better ways to deal with them. I also asked his mother to talk with Sam's teacher to see what she had noticed in her observations of Sam and his classmates.

Prior to the next session of our consultation Sam's mother forwarded me an email sent to her by Sam's teacher in response to her inquiry. The teacher wrote:

> Sam is a very bright boy who usually works hard and tries to follow all the rules, but in class he tends to be a very black or white thinker with strong opinions. He is often outspoken in criticizing other students for being wrong in their answers to questions or in comments they offer during discussion. He also tends to brag quite a bit about the many books he has read. And he's not hesitant about tattling to me when he sees someone not following the classroom rules. Sometimes his classmates express annoyance about these behaviors.

In our next session, Sam described an incident that had occurred in the intervening week. He told how three boys were walking toward him side by side. As they approached him they all "accidentally" bumped into him knocking his books out of his hands so his papers and notebooks were scattered all over the floor. As they walked away, one of the boys commented, "You just carry too many books all the time." As he told of the incident Sam was indignant that no other students in the crowded hall stopped to help him pick up his papers and notebooks. He said he had no idea about why the boys did that or why nobody else offered to help.

In this session Sam's father was hearing about this incident for the first time. Sam had told his mother about it, but she had not yet mentioned it to his father. His mother mumbled that she was sorry she had not previously mentioned the incident to his father. After Sam said he had no idea of why the boys had bumped into him, his father said:

> I have two reactions to what you just told us about that incident in the hall. My first reaction is that it pisses me off that they did that to you and also that you didn't tell me. My second reaction is that I don't think it is really a mystery why a lot of the boys don't like you and that they give you a hard time.

I have told you many times about what I see you doing in our basketball team and even our baseball team practices and games. You are too quick to tell other kids when they've made a mistake and too quick to tell them how they should have done something different. I'm the coach of your teams! You are not the coach!

Even if you know how they could improve their moves, it's not your job to tell other players when they have made a mistake or how they should correct it. I've told you that many times, but you still keep doing it. I don't understand why you don't get it. If you're doing anything like that when you're in school, it's easy to understand why other boys don't like you. This is going to be a huge problem in middle school.

Sam started crying and said to his father, "I really don't get what I'm doing that is so wrong. I just try to be helpful to other people." At that point it became clear that Sam really had not been able to understand what his father had tried to teach him about his interacting with other boys on his teams. He understood that his father was angry, but he was unable to see why his efforts to be helpful to other players on his team would be annoying to them as well as to his father.

At that point I told Sam that I needed some time to talk just with his parents. I asked him to wait in the waiting room and promised that soon we would invite him to rejoin us. I then spoke with Sam's parents telling them that the combination of the teacher's comments about Sam's interactions with his classmates, the story of the recent incident in the school hallway, and his father's description of the problems at the basketball and baseball teams combined to make clear that Sam had an additional problem beyond his previously diagnosed ADHD. I told his parents that Sam also met diagnostic criteria for Asperger syndrome and then briefly explained what that syndrome involves.

After hearing my description of Asperger syndrome Sam's mother told me that she and her husband had spoken with Sam's teacher just yesterday because of Sam having gotten failing grades on several history and math tests recently. She summarized the teacher's remarks as follows:

> Sam has been doing much better in some of the things he had trouble with earlier this semester. He's much better now with organizing his stuff, being prepared for classes and getting his homework in. But he struggles sometimes to integrate what we are studying. He can learn specific pieces, "concept A" and "concept B" and concept "C," but when asked to put them together, he can't do it. We're just realizing that although he is very bright, Sam has a lot of difficulty in putting the pieces together and seeing how they interact. Right now it seems that he tends to be too literal or rigid in understanding some things, not getting the broader picture and how the specifics fit into it. That's not unusual for some children this age, but Sam is so bright in so many ways, it's sort of puzzling.

Sam's father responded:

I've been thinking since that meeting yesterday. I'm realizing that I've had a similar problem with Sam sometimes when I'm coaching him in basketball and baseball. He's actually a very good athlete for his age, he can hit the baseball well and he's excellent in shooting baskets. But he often doesn't understand strategy, how to adjust his moves to fit changes during a game. Most of the other kids pick that up much more easily.

Sam's mother responded by telling her husband that she felt he was too hard on Sam in his sports. She agreed that the sports were good for Sam and that he was able to take a lot of pride when he did well in them. Yet she felt that her husband often put too much pressure on Sam, like telling him to work toward the goal of scoring at least six points in each basketball game. During a recent game against a very challenging team Sam got very agitated when another player made a mistake that put the other team ahead. His father pulled him to the bench. Sam then went out of the gym into the school corridor and ran full speed up and down the hall. He told his parents he had to do that to get rid of his anger. His mother had been worried seeing Sam so upset in the middle of a game when it was not he who had made the error.

It is not unusual for parents of children with ADHD and/or Asperger syndrome to get caught in conflicting views about how to respond to the difficulties of their son or daughter. Often one parent emphasizes to the other that their son or daughter needs to learn how to comply more adequately with rules and expectations so they will be able to "make it" in the world. Meanwhile, the other parent may take a very different stance. Seeing that their child often feels burdened or hurt by multiple corrections from teachers, family members, or peers, that parent may emphasize, "He is so often criticized by everybody, teachers, friends, other family members, and us, don't you think that, at least at home, it's good for us to be patient with him?" Often this results in each parent polarizing against the other, taking a more extreme position. We agreed to have an additional session just for the parents to sort out their conflicting feelings about these issues which they said had been a recurrent problem between them.

Meanwhile, we brought Sam back into the room to explain that we now understood that it was often hard for him to know when to tell when he should make suggestions to other students or teammates and when that was not a good idea. We agreed that we would start doing some role play exercises in our next session so we could try to figure out how and why other kids often were mean to him.

In our next session Sam began by reporting that over recent weeks he had been quite successful in baseball. "I had at least one hit in every one of our last four games. Dad showed me a way to improve my swing and it worked." This was one of many times when it became clear that Sam's self-esteem was often boosted by his athletic skills. He had considerable athletic talent and his father had spent many hours over the years in helping Sam to develop and refine his skills for both baseball and basketball. Despite his occasional hassles with teammates, Sam often felt team support for his skilled contributions to their team's performance. He also told his parents and me that he was working on trying to stop telling other players what they had done wrong. Both parents praised him for improving on that.

As we were discussing his sports performance, Sam said to his father, "You know it really bothers me that you don't compliment me when I do something good on the field. With the other kids you often give them compliments on a good play or a good hit, but you don't do that for me." His father responded, "You're probably right. I try to be careful to avoid doing anything that might look like the coach is favoring his own kid. Maybe sometimes I go too much the other way. I'll try to watch that." It was helpful that Sam's father responded as he did to his son's criticism. It modeled a way to respond to criticism without getting overly defensive.

In our session a few weeks later I asked Sam how things had been going for him in his first few weeks of middle school. He reported that a couple of kids he had known in fifth grade had made teasing comments to him, but he had successfully used some advice his guidance counselor had given him:

> I had told him that some kids I knew last year in fifth were bothering me. He told me not to act all hurt or mad, but just to look them in the eye and say "Whatever ..." and then just walk away. Calmly. They actually did stop after that! He taught me that if I acted all wounded or acted mad, that would make them bother me more. I guess he was right. The other thing that helped was that I've been sitting at lunch with some of the kids I know from the baseball team last summer. They were actually friendly to me! That's a lot better than it was at lunch back in fifth grade.

The advice Sam's guidance counselor gave him was sensible and helpful. This was consistent with advice offered by Elizabeth Laugeson in her book *The Science of Making Friends*. She observed that many parents provide their children or adolescents with counterproductive advice about how to deal with teasing. They tend to suggest just walking away, or ignoring the person, or telling an adult—all of which are likely to bring on more teasing. Laugeson noted that

> Research suggests that when confronted with teasing, social savvy teens and adults simply act like what the person said doesn't bother them and give the impression that the teasing remark was rather lame or stupid ... They give a short verbal comeback that demonstrates their indifference. They might say something like "Whatever" or "Yeah, and?" or "Your point is?" or "Am I supposed to care?" or "Is that supposed to be funny?" or "Anyway ..."
>
> (Laugeson, 2013, pp. 250–251)

After a number of sessions with Sam and his parents, much of it elaborating on principles and strategies such as those described by Laugeson in her book, we gradually tapered off our therapy sessions because Sam had made considerable progress in his interactions with classmates in middle school and with teammates on the baseball and basketball teams where he continued to play with increasing skill and success. He began to invite some of his friends to join in activities at his home or in going together to watch live sporting events. Those friends often reciprocated and gradually Sam developed much more adequate and successful ways to interact with his peers.

Sam's ADHD impairments persisted in his schoolwork where his grades gradually improved from C's, D's, and F's to mostly A's, B's, and C's. We continued to work together to monitor and recommend necessary adjustments to Sam's medications as they were being prescribed by his pediatrician. Eventually we discontinued regularly scheduled sessions and agreed to do consultations simply on an "as needed" basis as he continued in high school where he was functioning much better.

Years later I was pleased to receive the following letter from Sam's mother:

> Since we haven't been to see you for a long time, I wanted to send you this update. Sam is now in his third year of college and in a study abroad program for this semester. Freshman year was probably the biggest adjustment with learning what was expected from each class. He was fortunate to be placed in a dorm with a nice group of students with similar interests. That group has stuck together through these years.
>
> Since then he has continued to improve his grades and last semester he made the Dean's List! Besides his courses he is doing an internship at a company where he is helping to make videos for gaming companies. He is thrilled!
>
> During the past two summers he has been a camp counselor teaching gaming to kids while he lived at the camp for six weeks and developed skills for working with young people as well as the staff. I believe he is respected by the staff and they have asked him to take on additional roles.
>
> It's hard to know what the years ahead will bring, but we feel Sam is on a good path and we appreciate all that you have done to help both of us and Sam to be better prepared for this journey.

Reflections on Sam and Beyond

Sam's story illustrates how some students with Asperger syndrome and ADHD can improve considerably in response to appropriate guidance, medication and support. One factor that was quite important for Sam was his substantial athletic abilities and his father's encouragement for him to play on competitive teams for both basketball and baseball. Many children with ADHD and Asperger syndrome lack the athletic abilities that Sam had. For them, participation in competitive sports may be exceedingly frustrating and humiliating because they do not have the skills or the interest to participate in team sports where their failure to perform adequately can bring considerable resentment and harassment by other players.

Those who are less able or less interested in team sports may benefit more from participating in individual sports such as tennis, wrestling, martial arts, swimming or a different type of team activity such as robotics, science fair competition, school newspaper or musical programs.

For Sam, his participation in team athletics was generally satisfying, especially as he learned how to avoid being too critical or condescending and thus less provocative to other players. It was also helpful that Sam's father was very sensitive in his coaching to avoid showing favoritism to his son in ways that could have brought problematic jealousy.

Sam continued to make good use of his medication once he and his parents recognized how to recognize rebound and how to provide detailed information to his prescriber so the timing and dosing of his medication could be adjusted for various changes in his schedule and his responses to the various doses. It is important for parents of children with ADHD and for all adolescents and adults with ADHD to familiarize themselves with factual information about medications used to treat ADHD so they can provide their prescriber important information about their responses to medications at particular doses and scheduling.

Although some physicians and nurse practitioners are well-informed about the art and science of prescribing medications used for ADHD, many prescribers have not been provided sufficient training for "fine-tuning" of these medications for each individual. Sometimes it is necessary to seek out a specialist, but often prescribers can improve the medication regimen for a person if given detailed information about how long doses last, what benefits are produced, what side effects are noticed in the morning or in afternoon or in evening. (Information about strategies for fine-tuning medications for ADHD is provided in my book *Outside the Box: Rethinking ADD/ADHD*; Brown, 2017.)

4   Bella

I've read about Asperger's and I think I've got it. I don't like any of the kids in my class. I think they're pretentious and rude. They think I'm always in another world, and I am. I like to isolate myself and just read or write stories or songs or play games or my guitar. I used to get good grades, but this year I'm not getting much work done. And next year, there's high school.

Bella, a 13-year-old girl enrolled in eighth grade, was carrying a large stuffed animal when she came with her mother for her first consultation with me. When I asked why she had come to see me, she did not hesitate:

I run away from my work because I feel I'll never be able to get it done. My homework in every subject has been piling up for the past few months. I used to get good grades, but this year I'm not getting much work done. I feel like I'm suffocating. And next year there's high school.

Three years prior to that session, when she was ten years old, Bella had been evaluated by an experienced child psychiatrist who found her to be "a bright and talented girl who suffers from significant difficulties with executive functioning and meets diagnostic criteria for ADHD." She was started on a regimen of medication for ADHD, which did not prove helpful, so it was stopped, and no other medications for ADHD were tried.

Two years later Bella's mother sought evaluation for Bella with an experienced child psychologist who found that Bella was having frequent episodes of irritable mood and anger toward her mother. In his summary of that initial evaluation the psychologist noted:

Bella's mother reports that Bella has been increasingly moody and has had more frequent episodes of anger over the past year. She has been stressed, often lashing out at her mother with episodes of yelling, sulking, crying and restlessness on a near-daily basis. During such episodes she has made statements such as "What's the point of living?" and "I'm just going to kill myself" though she has never engaged in any self-harm behaviors, violence or aggression. She has also been isolative, not wanting to go to

DOI: 10.4324/9781003141976-7

after school activities or music lessons. Mother said Bella wants only to stay at home and play on the computer.

That doctor did not find evidence of ADHD in Bella; he decided that Bella was suffering from Generalized Anxiety Disorder. She was put on a new medication for anxiety. That coincided with Bella transitioning into middle school where she was in rotating classes with seven different teachers each day. Her frustration and irritability persisted, her grades were declining, and she was continuing to feel overwhelmed.

One year after that evaluation Bella came with her mother for consultation with me. In her opening comments of our first conversation, I was impressed by Bella's articulate and dramatic statement about her declining grades and her feeling like she was suffocating under a growing pile of unfinished work. I was also struck by her carrying the large stuffed animal and by her comment "And next year there's high school," a phrase that was spoken in an ominous tone. The juxtaposition of her holding the large stuffed animal and the tone of her mentioning her transition to high school was notable. In that moment the stuffed animal she was clutching seemed to be a symbol of her unreadiness and her fears of the transition to come.

Many adolescents enthusiastically look forward to the move from middle school to high school. Yet while they welcome the transition as an entry into the more interesting world of adolescence, for many that transition is also intimidating because they are moving from being the oldest students in their school to begin their next year where they become the youngest students in a building with other students who are one to four years older, most of whom are physically more mature, and some of whom are already licensed drivers.

I asked Bella what she did for fun when not in school. She explained that she loved to read and that she enjoyed writing stories and songs; she said she also spent a lot of time playing Minecraft and other video games, some of which involved developing roles for various characters. She also mentioned that she did not have many friends at school: "I don't like those kids. They're pretentious, rude and they ridicule me." When I asked how she thought her classmates would describe her, she responded "stupid," "introverted," "always in another world," and "antisocial."

I asked Bella to describe herself. She responded "I've always been an escapist. I go to the computer so I don't get into feeling overwhelmed. Emotions I have scare me. A lot of emotions I don't understand. I'm scared."

My impression at that time was that although Bella presented herself as being socially isolated as a choice due to her feeling superior to her classmates, she seemed, in fact, to suffer from significant social anxiety, quite excessively worried about what others may think of her and avoiding contact with peers except in situations such as school where her participation was required. Otherwise she preferred to take refuge in reading intensively and in role-playing video games.

Later I asked Bella's mother to ask each of her teachers to write a brief note about their observations of Bella with her classmates. Below are some of their responses:

Bella interacts little with her classmates. In classes she focuses on things she finds interesting ... at times I find her writing in her notebook or reading. During class discussions she may focus on what's being discussed and participate or she may ask a question that is off topic ... she seems to say whatever is on her mind regardless of how she may be perceived by others. She seems to lack a filter in public settings ... her classmates have come to accept Bella's quirky and somewhat offbeat personality.

Another teacher reported:

Bella's ability to grasp the subtleties and nuances of the French language is refreshing. Her patience and attention to detail goes beyond her years. At times she falls behind and loses interest in her work ... she constantly has a book in front of her. Her interaction with other students seems somewhat limited. The reception of other students to her seems to be somewhat guarded. She has her own agenda and makes it apparent.

A different teacher described how "Bella chooses not to interact with other kids":

When Bella is put into groups, she moves her table away from the other students and reads her book. She does not participate in any one-on-one conversation or even in group conversations. Bella will purposely call out in class causing a distraction. Sometimes the purpose is to make students laugh, and at other times it will be to elicit a different reaction from other students.

Reports from Bella's other teachers were quite similar in emphasizing her lack of interaction with classmates while acknowledging that she inconsistently demonstrated academic strengths.

Bella is an only child who lives with her mother, who owns and operates a small business; she has had no contact with her father since birth. Her parents had never been married and her father had not maintained any contact with Bella or her mother.

In our initial session Bella's mother expressed concern that Bella had been spending too much time each day online, typically playing video games for at least four hours, often more, each day. She noted that Bella had always had sensory processing issues such as being over-sensitive to certain kinds of lights, sounds and smells. He mother also reported that Bella doesn't like to be touched, has a low tolerance for pain, and often tends to avoid social interactions with anyone who is not already familiar to her. These sensitivities are not uncommon among children or adults with autism or Asperger syndrome.

Bella did not disagree with any of those observations by her mother, but she strenuously objected to her mother's saying that she had no friends. Bella responded: "It's true that I have no friends at school, but I have four friends that I'm close to online. I love them! Before these few people, I don't know how I survived. I can get into deep conversations with them!" It seemed clear that at that time Bella felt comfortable in peer social interactions only when the relationship was online with someone she was not likely ever to encounter face to face.

Despite her current social and academic difficulties, Bella demonstrated impressive strengths. Bella was quite open and articulate in talking with me throughout her evaluation and she worked diligently on academic and ability testing I did with her. On the Wechsler Intelligence Scale for Children–Fifth Edition her verbal comprehension abilities exceeded those of 99% of her age mates. On the other components of that IQ test, her scores were lower, but in the average range, while she scored in the low average range, below 77% of her peers, on measures of processing speed. Only about 2% of children her age have such a wide discrepancy between their verbal comprehension ability and their processing speed ability.

On testing for her academic achievement levels, Bella scored at the 99th percentile for reading, and at the 93rd percentile for math and for written expression. One of the test tasks for written expression required Bella to write a brief essay about her favorite game and to give three reasons why she liked that game. Below is what Bella wrote as the opening paragraph of her response to the test question:

> Picture a universe with infinite possibilities only restrained by the bounds of your imagination. Where there are no rules, no predetermined objectives aside from those you choose. That, my presumably skeptical friend, is Minecraft. With savannahs dotted with bushes and acacias to plateaus that cut through the clouds, the diverse landscapes are a sight to behold.

These sentences are impressive for a 13-year-old student, particularly when produced within less than ten minutes with no preparation. However, at the time of our initial consultation Bella had rarely been producing such written work with any consistency in her classes.

Bella had been diagnosed with ADHD two years prior to our consultation, but to assess her current level of impairment from ADHD I asked for her responses to my Brown Executive Function/Attention Rating Scale; I asked her mother and several of her teachers to rate Bella on that same scale. Responses from Bella, her mother and her teachers all indicated high probability of ADHD-related executive function impairments.

To assess Bella's strengths and difficulties with social interactions I used the Social Responsiveness Scale (SRS-2). This 65-item rating scale inquires about the individual's ability to interact and respond to others in socially appropriate ways. Responses are compared with norms for age and gender. This well-researched instrument indicates deficiencies in reciprocal social behavior that may range from severe or moderate forms of autistic spectrum disorder to mild impairments which may interfere in everyday social interactions with peers or adults.

Some items in the SRS-2 inquire about the extent to which the individual recognizes, correctly interprets, and responds to social cues, e.g. "Is socially awkward even when trying to be polite." "Doesn't recognize when others are trying to take advantage of him/her." Other items query regarding stereotypic behaviors or restricted range of interests, e.g. "When under stress shows rigid, inflexible patterns of behavior that seem odd." "Can't get his mind off something once he starts thinking about it." Additional items question for language deficits, such as "Takes things too literally and doesn't get the real meaning of a conversation."

Responses from Bella and her mother to items of the SRS-2 gave clear indication of a pattern of difficulties in social responsiveness that strongly supported my impression from our clinical interviews and the teacher reports that, in addition to the previously diagnosed ADHD and anxiety problems, Bella also met diagnostic criteria for Asperger syndrome as they appeared in the DSM-IV. Her total score on the SRS-2 was in the range which the manual for the test described as "indicating deficiencies in reciprocal social behavior that are clinically significant and lead to severe interference with everyday social interactions. Such scores are strongly associated with clinical diagnosis of an autism spectrum disorder."

Near the end of our initial consultation, and before I had offered any diagnosis for her, Bella handed me a note she had written in anticipation of our meeting. It read as follows:

> Some reasons (not excuses) as to why I struggle in school[:]
>
> ADHD: even with the medication I still have a tendency to doze off, get distracted and PROCRASTINATE. I can't help it. This the way I've always been. Sometimes I get called on out of the blue to answer a question I didn't even hear. It's absolutely mortifying which brings me to my next point—the crippling (medically diagnosed) anxiety. I've suffered from it for longer than I can remember. When there is a lot for me to work on, I get spooked and hide from it. Procrastination. I do that when logic tells me otherwise because facing the reality of such work gets me overwhelmed.
>
> Believe it or not, I legitimately care. I am not stupid nor am I unintelligent (not that anyone thinks that). Yes, I procrastinate, but this is not the work of a lazy adolescent. More because of a variety of disorders that are not yet adequately dealt with. I'd like to request some extra help. I need a real person to sit there and help me solve the specific problems, especially in math. Yet I fear that if I do get a tutor, I'll end up annoying them because of my slowness. Thank you. From a well-meaning but (currently) lousy student.

I thanked Bella for her note and told her that she was certainly not a lazy or unintelligent student and that I could see that she did indeed care about her work. I also agreed that her ADHD was not yet adequately treated, that we needed to make some adjustments to fine-tune her medications so they would work more effectively for her. I also acknowledged her chronic problem with anxiety. Then I mentioned that I thought her anxiety might be especially intense during this eighth grade year when she was trying to get herself ready to go to high school. She nodded agreement.

At that point I told her that I thought there might be one additional piece that was making her especially nervous about preparing for high school—I asked if she had ever heard of Asperger syndrome. She smiled broadly and said "Yes, I've read about it! I think I have it!" We then discussed what Asperger syndrome involves. I suggested that despite her being very bright about many things, she apparently did not yet understand how to interact with other students her age and older high school students in a comfortable way that would allow her to make and keep friends while avoiding being excessively teased or ridiculed. I suggested that her difficulty in understanding social interactions with other kids was intensifying her anxiety about entering high school. Bella, her mother, and I agreed to work together to develop a plan to help her.

One component of that plan was a series of therapy sessions in which Bella and I role-played past or recent interactions she recalled from her interactions with classmates and teachers. We tried out alternative responses she could make in such situations and considered which were most likely to be helpful and which were more likely to create misunderstanding. We also role-played many of those situations with role-reversal where she took the role of the other student and I played out variations of how she had previously handled such situations. In those scenarios Bella seemed quick to pick up why others might react with frustration as they did to some of her interactions with them.

Another aspect of our treatment plan was to arrange for Bella to have adjustments made to the medications she had previously been taking for anxiety while also starting her on a new regimen of medications to address her ADHD impairments. With the help of a psychiatrist she had previously seen we were able to find a dosing plan for ADHD medications that Bella found quite effective for improving her ADHD symptoms during the school day and also in late afternoon when she needed to do homework and to study. She had not responded well to Vyvanse, she tended to do much better on Adderall-XR, an extended release stimulant which has a more rapidly ascending curve as it initiates each of its two phases.

Some people respond better to the smoother release of Vyvanse while others do much better on Adderall, which is very similar in its ingredients, but different in its delivery system. For Bella, the Adderall-XR lost its effectiveness shortly before the end of the school day so she needed an a "booster dose" of Adderall (not XR) to extend coverage into late afternoon and early evening.

Another support was that her mother arranged for Bella to have tutoring sessions twice weekly for the remainder of the semester in middle school with a private tutor at home.

A third aspect of our plan was to work with staff of the high school she was going to attend to develop some advance planning for her transition. She made an early visit to the high school she was going to attend. There she had a guided tour and was given opportunity to meet with the counselor who would be working with her. He and other school staff worked with Bella, her mother, and me to establish an Individualized Educational Plan to arrange for Bella to get accommodations for extended time on tests and exams, to have one class period daily in a small group to receive resource support with a special education teacher and to meet once weekly for an individual counseling session with her guidance counselor.

With these various supports, Bella made some rapid and persistent improvements. She passed all of her eighth grade classes with grades of A or B. Her first semester of high school was completed with grades of A in History, French, and Music, B grades in Science and Social Studies, and a C in Geometry. She also became active in the school's orchestra and in the very active theatre department. There she had begun to develop friendships with a number of other students whose interests in music and theatre she shared.

Bella is an example of a student who met diagnostic criteria for Asperger syndrome and for social anxiety and ADHD who had serious trouble preparing for the transition to high school. With appropriate support she successfully made the transition to high school and began to thrive not only academically, but also socially. By the end of the first semester of her junior year she had earned grades that were all A's except for a C in Physics while her scores on the national PSAT exam placed her in the 98th percentile for reading and writing and in the 66th percentile for math for an overall score at the 91st percentile nationally.

Reflections on Bella and Beyond

Bella is a girl who clearly met diagnostic criteria for both ADHD and Asperger syndrome. She also fully met diagnostic criteria for social anxiety which is not like generalized anxiety where the person worries about many different things. Simply put, social anxiety is characterized by severely excessive worry about how others might be thinking about and judging oneself. Usually it is also characterized by avoidance of situations in which one anticipates being seen in an unfavorable light by others, even where the others may be total strangers. Some with Asperger syndrome have significant social anxiety while others do not.

Thus far there has not been much research study of girls with Asperger syndrome, but there have been some autobiographical accounts by women who have articulately described their experiences in growing up with Asperger syndrome. One example is Cynthia Kim's book *Nerdy, Shy, and Socially Inappropriate* (Kim, 2015), quoted in Chapter 1 of this book. She reports that she did not know she had Asperger syndrome until she was 40 years old, happily married, a successful small business owner and proud mother of a daughter. She came to know about Asperger syndrome from a radio discussion about it. As she listened, she recognized that what was being described in that program described aspects of herself which, despite her successes, had continued to be problematic for her since childhood:

I was the bookish, nerdy kid. The quirky teenager who loved karate and knew far too many random facts. I was always the quiet one, too shy to speak up in class, too shy to chase after boys or go to parties. I was the kid with weird friends and the weirder habits ... I could fill pages with humiliating memories of being bullied ... I took what the bullies doled out and told no one ... [then] one day when one of the mean girls in the neighborhood said something nasty to me, I said something nasty right back ... [thereafter] I resorted to bullying other kids in the absence of better coping strategies.

(Kim, 2015, pp. 18, 26 29)

Kim claims that Asperger syndrome often looks different in girls than in boys, though she notes that there are also differences among those girls. She notes that girls with Asperger syndrome tend to be more shy and less likely to act out than most boys with this syndrome. Yet the girls also tend to be more controlling in their interactions with peers. She also claims that girls with the syndrome tend to be more motivated to mimic socially acceptable behaviors in ways that make them less noticeable as different from most of their peers. However, she also recognizes that their lack of really understanding social expectations often results in social isolation that results in bullying and makes these girls more noticeable to teachers or parents. When she was placed in classes for talented and gifted children, she found more children like herself with whom she could be more comfortable than in the general population of her school. Bella had similar experiences when she got into high school where there more opportunities for her in music and theatre activities where she could associate with students with similar interests. In providing evaluation and treatment for individuals with Asperger syndrome and ADHD it is very important to recognize their strengths as well as their difficulties and to try to help them find ways to engage their strengths in their interactions with others.

One issue important in Bella's life was the fact that she had never had any contract with her father and had virtually no information about him. In my initial conversation with Bella and her mother, I inquired about her father. She explained that, until quite recently she had been told that her father had died shortly after her conception and before her birth. However, a few days before our initial consultation Bella had learned from her mother that the father was not actually dead. He had abandoned her mother before Bella was born and had been consistently out of contact with her mother ever since.

As we discussed this in my office, Bella asked her mother if there might be a way to contact her father just to find out a little bit more about him now. With my encouragement, her mother agreed to try to get in touch with his parents, who lived over 1000 miles away. This soon led to Bella's mother speaking directly with him by phone. She reported that he was very pleased to hear about Bella, felt guilty about having abandoned them, and would be glad to talk with Bella by phone.

In our next session Bella happily reported that over the past week she had enjoyed several phone conversations with her father and was hoping to travel with her mother to go and visit him and her paternal grandparents sometime soon. That trip occurred a couple of months after we had begun Bella's treatment. Following the trip Bella reported that she had been nervous before meeting him and his parents, but when she and her mother actually met them she quickly felt comfortable with him and her newly discovered grandparents. She said, "He's really nice now and I'm glad I finally know him. I want to stay in touch with him, but that does not totally erase the fact that he left us and did not ever get in touch until my mother reached out to him." This issue and the related issue of why her mother had so long persisted in saying he was dead were topics we discussed in detail over the course of Bella's treatment.

5 Jeremy

My husband and I can't agree on how to deal with our high-IQ son who is now in tenth grade. He has ADHD and is missing too many days of school. He complains of having a headache or stomachache and then his father lets him stay home when he's not really sick. He has no friends and is avoiding school to get away from the work and the kids who tease him. He just reads or plays video games all day. My husband is unemployed so he stays home while I have to leave early to get to my job which is our only income. What can I do?

Near the end of February in his eighth grade year, 13-year-old Jeremy came with his mother for an initial consultation with me. He was somewhat thin, but tall for his age; he wore his hair pulled back in a ponytail. Jeremy's mother explained that teachers had always identified her son as exceptionally bright, but extremely inconsistent in paying attention, following directions and doing his work. Jeremy spoke up saying that he knew he had ADHD, but that he could not control it.

To evaluate his current level of ADHD difficulties I asked Jeremy and his mother to respond to items from my Brown Executive Function/Attention Rating Scale. Their responses were almost identical in reporting significant difficulties in all six clusters of functions: activation, focus, effort, emotion, memory, and action. Both also provided many convincing examples of specific problems to confirm the ADHD diagnosis. After we all agreed that Jeremy met diagnostic criteria for ADHD, his mother spoke more directly about his immediate difficulties in school.

She was very concerned because Jeremy had essentially gone "on strike" in school since the end of Christmas vacation. He now spent most of his time in class ignoring assignments and discussions, reading unassigned books, or keeping his head down on his desk as though he were sleeping. He had completed virtually no classwork and no homework in the preceding two months. She also noted that at home over recent months Jeremy was doing virtually nothing except immersing himself in many hours of playing video games every day.

When I asked Jeremy why he was "on strike" he replied angrily:

It's because of the teachers and the special ed stuff! They tell me I'm smart and then they treat me like I'm retarded! I'm not going to respect

DOI: 10.4324/9781003141976-8

them and do what they want me to do until they change what they're doing and treat me with respect!

I asked for an example of what he was complaining about. Jeremy said that because he had not been completing many assignments for the first semester, he was one of just a few in his class who were being quite obviously monitored and "*assisted*" by a special education teacher who worked in his classroom. He complained:

> She keeps coming over to my desk to check on my work and is always reminding me what I should be doing. It's humiliating. It started just after Christmas vacation because they want me to improve and get ready to start high school in the fall. But it's not going to work! I don't need special education help now and I won't accept it in high school either, regardless of what they do.

At that point I told Jeremy that I saw no way in which his current strategy could get him what he wanted. I reminded him that the grown-ups are running the world, not the children. I told him that if he persisted in his strike, he would soon be getting even more intensive special education and possibly get transferred to a specialized school for students with serious problems. I asked if he could see any way he could change that might help him to improve his situation at school.

Jeremy put his head down and started to cry. "I'm broken … what's the point? I'll never amount to anything." I told him that I saw him as a very bright boy who was not broken, but that he did need to make some significant changes if he wanted to get things to change for him. I suggested that he stop his strike immediately and do his best each day to complete his class work and homework. I told him that if he could do that consistently for one full week, I would ask to have the special education services stopped for the following week. If he continued to perform in that way in the next week, he could keep himself free of the special ed services for the following week, and so on for the remainder of the semester. I promised that if he performed like a serious student for the remaining weeks of the semester, I would recommend that he have no special education services in high school, so long as he continued to perform adequately.

To support this plan I suggested that Jeremy begin seeing me for psychotherapy on a weekly basis for a while so we could talk together about school and whatever else seemed important. I also told him that I would work with him, his parents, and his physician to try to find a new medication regimen that might help to improve his ADHD impairments, his anxiety, and his feeling so hopelessly depressed. Jeremy tried to bargain with me, saying he wanted the special ed services stopped immediately. I told him there was no way that would happen, that he needed first to show that he was ending his strike and then to continue to do his part in order to get what he wanted.

I was quite certain that even if Jeremy could be successful in stopping his strike and working productively for the remaining three months of the semester, there were other significant underlying problems that would need to be addressed. His difficulties in school had been significant long before his strike and he had already tried some medications for ADHD which had to be discontinued because of adverse effects.

Prior to that first meeting Jeremy's mother had sent me a copy of a report written four years earlier, as Jeremy was completing fourth grade. His classroom teacher wrote in that report:

> Jeremy continues to demonstrate difficulty sustaining his attention long enough to sit through lessons, participate in discussions, begin and complete assignments, and to take advantage of small group and one-on-one teaching. Because of this, Jeremy has not been able to apply the many academic strengths he possesses ... He is visibly distracted throughout the school day and has difficulty sitting in his seat ... He reads incessantly and routinely creates elaborate doodles all over his work, tiny battle scenes in great detail ... He has a very vivid imagination and loves to get lost inside the world of a book ... He reads at a break-neck pace, finding it very difficult to slow down even when asked to ... He is a smart, sweet, gentle boy who has been dealing with so much this year.

Soon after that report from his fourth grade teacher Jeremy had been evaluated and diagnosed with ADHD by his pediatrician who prescribed a trial of Vyvanse and then Focalin, both at rather high doses that were not adjusted. Jeremy was not able to tolerate the side-effects of either, so the medication was stopped. He was then put on a low dose of Sertraline, an SSRI which helped to reduce his anxiety a bit, but it did nothing for his ADHD impairments. He apparently had a very sensitive body chemistry, which I expected to make it difficult to get an adequate medication regimen.

From the way he interacted with his mother and with me, as well as from his inability to see for himself that his strike was totally counter-productive, I had a strong suspicion that Jeremy also had Asperger syndrome. I administered the Social Responsiveness Scale–2nd edition (SRS-2) which confirmed my suspicion that Jeremy had rather severe symptoms of impairments in social awareness and social communication that were "strongly associated with a clinical diagnosis of an autism spectrum disorder." Jeremy, his mother, and I talked about what Asperger syndrome involves and how it complicated his functioning with classmates as well as with teachers and his family. Jeremy responded to this in quite a positive way. He said "It's actually helpful to know this. I figured my problem wasn't just regular ADHD."

From my earlier conversation with Jeremy's mother I had learned that there were also some other complicated problems in their family. She was a very bright and well-educated corporate executive with an MBA who, when quite young, had married a man whom she had found appealing despite his having been unable to complete a second year of college due to ADHD and related learning problems. For some years he had been employed selling insurance, but he lost that job due to excessive drinking which got worse after loss of the job. He had stopped drinking about two years ago, but not been employed for several years before my involvement with the family. He remained a stay-at-home father caring for their two children but doing little to search for any steady employment for himself.

The couple had attempted marital therapy, but the husband eventually refused to continue. Jeremy's mother told me that she was very frustrated with their marriage, but did not want to initiate a divorce because both Jeremy and his younger sister were quite attached to their father and because his caring for the children allowed her to work full-time to support their family. She also mentioned that her husband had a twin brother who had suffered a "nervous breakdown" in early adulthood that was diagnosed as schizophrenia; that brother was currently living in a group home setting for psychiatric patients. Jeremy's mother told me privately that her husband often acted quite moody. She suspected that her husband was depressed and also "might have some kind of mental illness."

Both parents and I were pleased that Jeremy responded to my challenge and ended his strike behavior, earning relief from the special ed support that he had resented so much. Over the following weeks he continued his progress and seemed to be benefitting from a retrial of Vyvanse which he was able to tolerate after starting with a minimal 10 mg dose and then gradually increasing it to an effective dose of 40 mg followed by a booster dose of 10 mg short-acting Dexedrine after school to help with homework. Jeremy also made good use of our psychotherapy sessions, half of which included his mother and sometimes also his father; Jeremy spoke with me individually for the other half of each session.

As a result of his significant progress over the last few months of the semester, Jeremy's school agreed to allow him to enroll in the high school without any special education support, though they stipulated that such support could readily be arranged during the school year if needed. In September Jeremy began his freshman year getting to all his classes; in the second week he actually requested that he be placed in a higher level of math because the class he had been assigned was too easy for him. He was moved up in math. His first quarter grades were mostly B's with just one C. He also began meeting with a few friends to play Dungeons and Dragons once a week.

Shortly after the first quarter was completed, Jeremy's mother got frightening news. She had found a lump in her breast. Biopsy of the tumor indicated stage 2 cancer. Immediately she began a course of chemotherapy which caused her to feel quite sick after each weekly treatment, but she continued to work, albeit on a reduced schedule. After she told her husband and children about this, both her husband and Jeremy became depressed and withdrawn from her while her daughter was quite anxious and increasingly clingy with her mother. Week after week the mother cycled through her chemo treatments, feeling totally exhausted for a day or two after each one and then regaining some strength, only to feel totally wiped out again after less than a week. She also lost her hair and began wearing a wig. After a second course of chemo, it was decided that she needed a double mastectomy.

After the surgery, Jeremy's mother struggled with complications which required an additional surgery and left her quite weak, extending the duration of her post-operative recovery. For those weeks while she was at home, mostly in bed, the father and both children were fully supportive. After she returned to work, her husband began to report that he was having considerable difficulty with sleeping. He asked me to speak with his physician to see if he could get some medication to help with his sleep problems and increasing feelings of depression. I spoke with his doctor who readily agreed to prescribe an appropriate antidepressant for the father which helped to improve his sleep problems.

Soon after his mother was back at work, Jeremy began to avoid school with a variety of vague complaints about headache or stomachache. His mother asked her husband to support and encourage Jeremy to get to school every day when he was not obviously very ill. He agreed to do this, but, in fact, the father frequently allowed Jeremy to skip school despite the mother's insistence that he attend regularly. Jeremy's mother became increasing worried about Jeremy's erratic attendance and was progressively more angry with her husband for his failure to support Jeremy in getting to his classes. Jeremy responded with intense worry about his father and angrily told his mother, "You are always mad at him, you're breaking him."

In my therapy sessions with Jeremy during this period we discussed his worries about his mother and his wondering whether her cancer would eventually come back. He also spoke about his bigger worries about his father and himself. He described how his father seemed increasingly depressed; he was worried that his father might go back to excessive drinking.

Jeremy also spoke about how he was worried about himself because he had begun occasionally to hear voices in his head, some of which were quite pessimistic while other voices were more encouraging. He said that he knew the voices were in his own thoughts and not coming from outside him, but he feared that he might be getting psychotic like his father's brother was.

After questioning for more details about the voices, I reassured Jeremy that I felt quite certain that he was not going to be having severe mental problems like his uncle. I also told him that we would arrange for him to take a small dose of risperidone, an anti-psychotic medication for a while to help get rid of the voices while we worked together to help him deal with the stresses of his mother's health problems and his father's increased depression. I also encouraged him to continue his progress in attending classes regularly and in completing assignments.

Meanwhile, Jeremy's mother's condition worsened. She needed to return to the hospital for additional surgery, after which she recovered slowly over another month, unable to return to work. During that period Jeremy attended classes with few absences and was able to improve most of his grades. He also became very preoccupied with caring for two pet ferrets that his father had purchased for him. He spent considerable time caring for and playing with the ferrets while keeping them in a cage the rest of the time to prevent them from chewing furniture and nipping at other members of the family.

After several weeks Jeremy announced that his ferrets needed more companionship from other ferrets. His mother told him emphatically that they could not get more ferrets because the contract for rental of their home stipulated no pets. She feared that if the landlord discovered the ferrets, it could cost them financial penalties or possibly eviction. When his mother went back to work a couple of weeks later, his father yielded to Jeremy's request to go to look at ferrets in the store where their two ferrets had been purchased. They came back with three more ferrets.

When she arrived home from work that day and saw the new ferrets, Jeremy's mother was furious. She felt betrayed by her husband's going against her wishes and ignoring her fears of problems with the landlord. Jeremy insisted that all of the ferrets must be kept: "They are my children." He threatened that if his mother had them removed, he would run away or kill himself. His father tried to reassure his wife that the five ferrets would not be any more of a problem that the two had been and that they would be good for Jeremy.

Within a few days it became clear that five ferrets were altogether too much for the family to manage. They ran around the house chewing on furniture and ripping up pillows. They were also nipping with their sharp teeth on the feet of family members. Moreover, their excrement was causing a bad smell throughout the house. Mother threatened that if the three new ferrets were not removed from the house she was going to leave and stay with a friend until they were gotten rid of. Jeremy had a protracted tantrum with multiple threats, but one day after the father returned them to the seller while Jeremy was at school, the boy reluctantly accepted the fact that the three new ferrets were now gone and would not be allowed back.

After he spent a couple of therapy sessions complaining about the loss of the three ferrets Jeremy questioned me about OCD (obsessive compulsive disorder), something we had not previously discussed. He told me that for many years he had felt compulsions to arrange things in symmetrical patterns and to complete tasks that most other people would not need to complete. He had to arrange food on his plate so that no one food would touch any other; he also said that he had to straighten any picture that was hanging the least bit crooked. He tried to avoid stepping on the lines of tiled floors and felt compelled to swing each arm in an identical way when he walked. He also reported that it was very difficult for him to leave any written sentence unfinished or to put away any puzzle before it was completely assembled.

Jeremy told me that his maternal grandmother had been diagnosed with OCD and continued to have it all her life. I saw this as one layer of a more subtle fear: his fear of struggling with the psychiatric problems of his paternal uncle and, perhaps also, fear of being like his father in being unable to complete college or to hold a job.

I noted his concern about inheriting disorders from other family members. He acknowledged that the OCD was not such a big problem currently, that he was more worried about being like his father's brother who had not been able to complete college, to hold a job, or to live independently. Yet he noted that the risperidone seemed to be helping to get rid of the voices he had been hearing in his head. I told him that I expected that the voices would continue to go away and that if his OCD began to feel like a big problem we could certainly find a way to deal with it. However, I emphasized that his primary problem at present was, in spite of family stresses, to maintain steady attendance and participation in his classes and to put significant effort into completing class work and homework. He did this reasonably well for the rest of the semester.

Shortly after the end of that spring semester, I was going to be relocating from the east coast to the west coast. While I was planning after my move to continue treatment with some of my patients via telehealth, I felt that Jeremy and his family needed to have a therapist nearby whom they could continue to see in person. We arranged for the child psychiatrist who had been prescribing for him to continue to manage his medications. We also agreed that Jeremy's parents would continue treatment for Jeremy and themselves with a local therapist, and that I would maintain contact with them via weekly online sessions for a couple of months while they established those arrangements. Within two months the new therapist was engaged and we terminated my work with Jeremy and his family. One year later I was glad to hear from Jeremy's mother and his new therapist that, although there were some continuing difficulties, Jeremy and his family were functioning considerably better and he had successfully completed his next year of high school.

Reflections on Jeremy and Beyond

This case example about Jeremy illustrates the importance of considering persons struggling with emotional and behavioral difficulties not simply as individuals, but also as members of a family. The family often has significant implicit and complicated impacts on each individual member as they react to one another and to the circumstances of their individual and shared daily life. In their book *Invisible Loyalties*, Boszormenyi-Nagy and Sparks (1973) provided excellent descriptions of how what appear to be simply individual problems often reflect complex unrecognized dynamics of guilt and unconscious obligations among family members.

Jeremy's difficulty in getting to school and difficulty in doing his work on a regular basis impacted each of his parents as well as his sister in multiple ways. It worried both of his parents and often frustrated his sister who sometimes felt that her brother was making the already fragile alliance between their parents even more shaky. At the same time, especially when Jeremy was being oppositional with his mother, the sister got increased positive attention from their mother who appreciated the daughter's being more compliant with usual expectations. Jeremy's sister also provided consistent affection and closeness to her mother while Jeremy often treated his mother with defiance and often overt hostility.

My conversations with Jeremy clearly showed that he was very worried about his father, especially when he overheard his mother expressing frustration and anger toward the father for his failure to insist that the boy regularly attend school. Jeremy's repeated desire to stay at home rather than to go to school seemed to be motivated not only by his wish to avoid negative interactions with classmates who teased and sometimes bullied him. His staying home from school also allowed him to provide support and companionship to his father, whom Jeremy saw as vulnerable and somewhat fragile, especially when he was angrily criticized by his wife. Jeremy sometimes gave indications of fearing not only that his father might resume excessive drinking, but also that his father might become incapacitated in other aspects of adult life as the father's brother had been.

Jeremy's worries about developing problems similar to his paternal uncle are an example of "struggle against identification" in which a family member may struggle, consciously and/or unconsciously, with persistent fears that they will develop significant impairments observed in another family member. It can be helpful to discuss such fears when they are apparent, but it is also important to help the worried family member to recognize that having a blood relative with a particular impairment does not make it inevitable that the same problems will occur in other family members, regardless of how close their kinship may be.

Jeremy tended to see his mother as quite strong relative to his father, almost invulnerable, until she was diagnosed with cancer. Throughout his mother's protracted struggles with cancer, Jeremy episodically showed his concern for her health and medical problems, but that concern often was not sufficient for him to ease up in his complaining to her about any restrictions she placed on him and about her often being critical and angry with his father. His comment to his mother that "You're breaking him" illustrates Jeremy's strong sense of his father's fragility.

One very helpful action of Jeremy's father was his decision to return the three ferrets despite Jeremy's dramatic demand that they had to stay. At that point Jeremy's mother was so frustrated that she threatened to go live elsewhere until the ferrets were removed. The father's returning those ferrets provided support for his wife and avoided the complicated problems that would have been likely for all four family members if the mother had moved out. Notably, Jeremy seemed to sense this because he offered no further protest about losing the three ferrets. It is important to see how family members who appear uninvolved or problematic sometimes find ways to contribute constructively to alleviating family problems.

6 Justin

Two years ago my grandson was struggling in middle school. Anytime a teacher pointed out even a minor error in his work or suggested adding more elaboration in a paper, he would start crying and walk out of the class unwilling to discuss the matter. He was never a trouble-maker, but he was painfully shy and withdrawn from other kids. He was good at math, but had a lot of trouble with any long reading or writing assignments. With support from special ed teachers, his counselor and prescribed medications he has now completed his first year of high school with grades all A or B and has made several friends.

Justin was in sixth grade, early in his first year of middle school, when his father and his maternal grandmother brought him to my clinic for an initial consultation. They explained that Justin's mother was unable to come because she was physically disabled due to a stroke she had suffered when Justin was 3 years old. Justin's father had taken some college courses and was employed as a construction worker; he was also the primary caretaker for his disabled wife and for Justin.

Justin's father and grandmother sought this consultation because they were very concerned about Justin's having a difficult adjustment to middle school. He was frequently bullied and shunned by classmates, had difficulty complying with school requirements, and had episodic "meltdowns." During those episodes he would hit himself, cry, bang his head repeatedly on his desk or against the cinder block wall and then leave the classroom. Most of those problematic behaviors occurred at school, seldom at home. His father and grandmother were worried that Justin might be placed in a self-contained special education classroom where he would be away from most other students.

I asked Justin to tell me about his experiences in school. He told me that he often was bullied, isolated, or rejected at school: "The kids all ignored me ever since I was in first grade, they acted like I wasn't even there. Now that I'm in middle school I have these episodes of getting so frustrated in class. It's all getting worse." He told me that he had no friends outside of school. He said that at home he enjoyed playing games on his Xbox, especially Minecraft, and that he enjoyed watching TV with his parents.

Several months prior to his initial consultation with me Justin had been diagnosed by his pediatrician as having ADHD. His father and grandmother

DOI: 10.4324/9781003141976-9

were opposed to the stimulant medication he had suggested. Instead they saw a naturopathic physician who prescribed a variety of diet supplements. He was also evaluated by an experienced speech/language specialist, who reported that Justin had a social pragmatic communication disorder, though she also wrote in her report that "ADHD is a major contributor to Justin's difficulties, especially his inability to relate to others and to meet social demands in age-appropriate ways."

Justin's father and grandmother reported that they were not satisfied with the diagnoses they had been given for Justin; they also mentioned that the homeo-pathic physician had recently told them that the diet supplements did not seem to be sufficiently effective. He suggested that they see me for a reconsideration of the diagnosis and consider the possibility of using prescribed medication.

I asked his father and grandmother what the school thought about Justin's difficulties. They reported that he had an Individualized Education Plan and was getting support from a special education teacher who was placed in his classroom to help Justin and one other student who had been recognized as needing special education services. The school's consulting child psychiatrist had evaluated Justin and decided that he had severe ADHD and problems with anxiety and depression.

After administering my rating scales and some further discussion I explained to Justin's father and grandmother that Justin clearly demonstrated ADHD impairments, but that he also some additional social difficulties that required further exploration. Meanwhile, I suggested a trial of guanfacine-ER, a non-sti-mulant medication approved for treating ADHD that is usually helpful for reducing excessive restlessness, emotional dysregulation, and impulsive behavior. They agreed to starting a trial of that medication and to continue for further evaluation. They also asked the teachers working with Justin to send weekly notes about their observations of Justin in class and his interactions with classmates. After a week on the minimal starting dose of 1 mg, without adverse effects we gradually increased the guanfacine-ER to a regimen of 3 mg daily.

Reports from Justin's teachers indicated that he continued to be quite inconsistent in completing homework assignments. Hearing this, his grand-mother proposed that she could pick Justin up most days after school and take him to her home where she would give him a snack and then encourage him to work on his homework and spend some time with her before she drove him home to his parents. Justin and his parents readily agreed to this plan which quickly became quite successful in helping Justin to become consistent in get-ting his homework completed while giving him frequent and enjoyable time with his grandmother.

Over the next few weeks Justin reported that the medication seemed to be helping him remain more calm during school. Email reports from his teachers indicated that Justin seemed more settled in class sessions and was working more productively. They were still seeing him often distracted and getting upset over apparently minor frustrations such as changes in scheduled activ-ities, feeling jealous over another student being recognized for good behavior, worrying excessively about whether he would be getting a good grade on an assignment, and panicking and stating that "I'm so dumb!" and walking out of the classroom when he was unable quickly to figure out a solution for a math problem. Reports from school indicated that Justin's teachers and support staff were quite patient and skilled in helping Justin to cope with such episodes of frustration. They also arranged for their BCBA behavioral consultant to observe Justin's classroom behaviors for segments of several days. Meanwhile, we added a small daily dose of methylphenidate, in addition to the guanfacine-ER, to help Justin sustain attention and effort for assignments.

I used the Social Responsiveness Scale–2 to collect information from Justin, his teachers, his parents and his grandmother about his social functioning. Items on that scale inquire about the extent to which the individual recognizes, correctly interprets, and responds to social cues; for example, "Is socially awkward even when trying to be polite," and "Doesn't recognize when others are trying to take advantage of him." Other items query regarding stereotypic behaviors or restricted range of interests, such as, "When under stress shows rigid, inflexible patterns of behavior that seem odd," and "Can't get his mind off something when he starts thinking about it." Additional items question for language deficits like "Takes things too literally and doesn't get the real meaning of a conversation."

Responses from Justin's teachers and family on this rating scale yielded scores indicating that they saw Justin as "having deficiencies in social behavior that are clinically significant and lead to substantial interference with everyday social interactions. Norms for the scale indicated that the scores reported were "strongly associated with a diagnosis of an autism spectrum disorder."

In reporting these data from the rating scales I emphasized that Justin was not being described as classically autistic, but as being a bright boy who was currently struggling with problems in understanding and interacting with others, especially his classmates, more than most other students his age. I explained our use of the term "Asperger syndrome" to describe such difficulties in those with average or above average intelligence. I also emphasized that with patience and sustained support it was likely that Justin could significantly improve his social understanding and interactions.

Around this time the school psychologist administered to Justin the Wechsler Intelligence Scale for Children–Fifth Edition (WISC-V) in preparation for his triennial evaluation. Results indicated that Justin's verbal comprehension score was in the high average range, stronger than 86% of his age mates; his score for fluid reasoning with visual puzzles was stronger than 88% of his peers. His index score for working memory was at the 58th percentile but his score for processing speed was very low, weaker than 91% of his peers. This pattern of strong verbal and visual skills accompanied by relatively weaker working memory and/or processing speed is often found in those with ADHD who have average or above-average IQ (Brown, Reichel and Quinlan, 2011b).

Results of that IQ test and other assessments were presented and discussed at the school's triennial review of Justin's IEP. At that meeting the school also presented results from classroom observations of Justin made by their BCBA behavior analyst. She identified four target behaviors: (1) calling out, off topic; (2) work refusal; (3) self-injurious behavior (e.g. hitting self in his head with a binder or fist); and (4) ripping up papers in frustration. She also prepared a behavior intervention plan to help Justin reduce the frequency of these problematic behaviors which he had engaged in for a long time.

The BCBA's plan gave teachers directions to help them reinforce Justin's efforts to change the target behaviors. It also provided a daily report card form for teachers to score for intervals each day when Justin was able to function appropriately without engaging in the target behaviors. He brought these reports home daily to show his grandmother when he went to her house each day; he then took them home so his parents could also commend him on his progress. Within a couple of months, the combination of the medication, the behavior intervention plan, and the combined reinforcing efforts of his grandmother and parents helped Justin to reduce those four problematic behaviors significantly. That success provided a big boost to his self-esteem. He had been painfully aware of the inappropriateness of those behaviors and was proud to have them diminished significantly before he moved up into seventh grade.

In addition to his behavioral improvements Justin also showed considerable improvement in his classwork and homework after he settled into the routine of visiting his grandmother daily to get his homework done. His grades throughout his seventh grade year were high enough to qualify him for the honor roll, a pattern of success he sustained throughout his seventh grade year.

During this period I continued to see Justin once every few weeks in split sessions to provide both individual psychotherapy and conjoint sessions with him, his father and his grandmother. In one of those individual sessions Justin asked if we could talk about something besides just school and family. I said "sure" and asked what other things he could suggest. He mentioned that at school they had watched a film about how kids get their "fast-growing period." I commented that I felt that was a good thing to talk about and asked him what they covered in the movie. He said, "Just about how your body changes in that fast-growing period and then stuff about how babies are made, stuff that all of us already know."

I asked what else he thought they should have covered in that class. Shyly he mumbled "I'm starting my fast-growing period already." I asked what signs of growth he had noticed in his body. He mentioned that he was developing some pubic hair and that his voice was deepening a bit. I talked a bit about how those changes come earlier for some kids and later for others. I also asked him if they had said anything about wet dreams or masturbation. He asked me what those words meant. After I briefly explained wet dreams and masturbation, Justin said:

> They didn't say anything about those things, that would have been embarrassing! Nobody talks about that, except I heard a couple of boys in gym class teasing a kid about how he jerks himself off every night. What does that mean? Sounds bad and nasty!

I took Justin's statement about "bad and nasty" as his way of asking if I felt that way about masturbation. I was also aware that, because he was quite isolated from social interaction with his peers, it was quite likely that he had not had much exposure to the mutual teasing and joking about sexuality and masturbation that commonly occurs in peer interactions of many early adolescent boys, normalizing such experiences.

I told him directly that I do not consider masturbation to be bad or nasty. I explained that most people in their early teens and beyond enjoy masturbating because it feels good and it doesn't do any harm. I explained that one does not have to "jerk off" nor does one need to avoid doing it. I noted that this is usually done privately, though sometimes people enjoy doing it with others. Justin then told me that he often enjoyed masturbating, especially since he had begun to experience ejaculation when he did it. He said he was glad to hear that it wasn't such a big deal. He was then ready to turn to another topic, though in subsequent sessions he readily spoke about sexual concerns from time to time.

During the second semester of his eighth grade year Justin continued his progress in controlling his behavior and getting his schoolwork done. This was not fully consistent; there were certainly occasional episodes when he regressed to his old behaviors, but these were usually brief and much less frequent.

In the middle of the second semester notices were sent to parents of all eighth grade students asking them to choose which of two local high schools they wanted to enroll their student in for the coming year. One was a general high school offering a traditional program to prepare students for college. The other was a vocational-technical school which offered a wide variety of technical specialties like carpentry, printing, auto mechanics, plumbing, and electronics. Over the course of their four years of high school students in the technical high school would spend half of their time doing academic subjects while they spent the rest of their school day learning content and practical skills related to whichever trade they chose for their specialty. Both schools had good reputations for what they provided to students.

Two of Justin's teachers suggested to Justin, his father and grandmother that the best choice for Justin would be the technical school. Justin felt demoralized because he assumed, not unreasonably, that the teachers were saying he was not likely to be successful in trying to prepare himself to go to college. He told his father and grandmother that most of his friends were going to the general high school. He told them that he was not interested in any of the trades taught at the technical school and that, even though he still had problems to work out, he did not want to go to the technical school. He wanted to prepare himself to go to college. After talking with several of Justin's other teachers and with me, Justin's father and grandmother decided to support Justin's plan to enroll in the general high school for the coming year.

The school social worker and several teachers who had worked with Justin throughout middle school strongly supported his plan to enroll in the general high school. One reminded him that in his most recent standardized achievement tests he had scored in the high average range for reading and written expression and solidly in the average range for math, better than many other students who would be going to that general high school. The social worker wrote that Justin "has made great improvements in impulse control since the start of his middle school career and is performing successfully academically with some support. Observations show that he is engaging in positive behaviors and engaging in a positive manner with peers."

Justin was quite anxious as the day for starting high school approached, but he coped well with adjusting to the much larger school and more demanding courses. He had one period daily in a learning center where he was provided extra support in organizing and monitoring his homework. His first quarter grades were all A's or B's except for algebra, which he failed for the first quarter due to problems with getting his homework done and having a teacher who was inexperienced and not very good at explaining new concepts. His family got him a math tutor. With that tutoring help he was able to make honors for his mid-year grades.

During the second semester of his freshman year Justin had a couple of difficult weeks when he was not completing his homework and he seemed somewhat depressed. He also refused to take a swimming test that was required for his gym class, even though he was actually a decent swimmer. Initially his grandmother and father thought that this depressed mood and work refusal were a reaction to a slight increase in Justin's medication that we had made two weeks earlier.

When I talked with Justin I asked him what had been going on for him over the past couple of weeks. Initially, he said "nothing special," but I challenged him, saying that I thought there must be a reason why things had gotten so difficult for him recently. He then put his head down and quietly began to cry. He then told me that his grandfather had been diagnosed with cancer. He was worried that his grandfather was going to die soon and that, if that happened, his grandmother, the one he visited virtually every day, might die soon afterward.

That was the first I had heard about his grandfather having cancer. I phoned the grandmother while Justin was with me. She explained that Justin must have overheard a conversation she had with his father. They had decided not to tell Justin about the cancer until the grandfather had surgery in the following week; they did not want to upset Justin until they found out the results of the surgery that was planned for the following week to remove the tumor. I put the phone on speaker so she could explain the situation to Justin directly.

Following that conversation Justin and I spoke about his worries about his grandfather and grandmother, recognizing the importance of both of them in his life. We also talked about how it was not possible to know whether this surgery might protect his grandfather so he could live a lot longer or whether the tumor would turn out to be a bad one so he would be increasingly ill and die quite soon. I emphasized the importance of family members helping each other during such difficult times. I helped him write and send an email to his grandfather saying how he was sad to hear about the cancer and how very much he was hoping and would be praying for his grandfather's recovery.

Fortunately, the surgery was successful and Justin's grandfather recovered. This experience provided a valuable opportunity for Justin to share openly with his family his deep, but rarely acknowledged love for them. After this experience, Justin resumed his consistency in completing his schoolwork. He also asked his parents for permission to take snowboarding lessons, the first time he had ever been willing to engage in any sport. His grades for the remainder of that school year kept him on the honor roll.

In talking with me at the end of that school year Justin told me that he felt good about changes in his social interaction. He said, "This year people don't ignore me so much as they used to. My reputation is getting better and there are several other kids that I talk with once in a while." I told Justin, his father, and his grandmother that I was very impressed by his progress both in his academic work and in his social interaction. He had come a very long way since we had begun working together while he was in sixth grade.

During the summer following his freshman year Justin worked successfully as a counselor-in-training at a day camp he had attended as a camper for the previous two summers. He did quite well as an assistant leader for a group of younger day campers. He then continued to work as a junior leader for younger participants in the local YMCA, an activity he continued throughout that year. Justin received frequent compliments from the leaders in the day camp and the YMCA program about how well he worked with their groups of younger children.

Throughout his sophomore year Justin's grades were almost all in the A or B range. Toward the end of that year he began talking about how he was getting interested in finding out about some of the colleges in the state where he might be able to study engineering. At that point he had taken a couple of computer-assisted design (CAD) courses and found that he enjoyed that work and was doing well in it. This was fully consistent with his performance on the "fluid reasoning" index of his IQ test where he had scored stronger than 88% of his age peers on national norms.

During that summer Justin, his father and his grandmother visited several colleges in their state. Justin reported that he really liked the large state university which reportedly had a very good engineering program. He also reported that if he could stay on the honor roll for the rest of high school, he would be able to get a full scholarship to attend that university. As this is being written Justin is continuing his progress academically and socially during his junior year of high school.

Reflections on Justin and Beyond

One very important factor in Justin's impressive social and academic progress from sixth grade through his junior year was the very active and consistent support provided by his grandmother. For several years she picked Justin up after school each day and brought him to her home for several hours. There she had lengthy conversations with him over an afternoon snack. They would discuss events of the school day and his interactions with his teachers and classmates while she also helped him to organize and get his homework done. This was crucially important because Justin's disabled mother was physically and emotionally unable to provide such support and his father was unable to get home from work until dinner time.

Justin's father was not uninvolved with him. He consulted regularly with the grandmother and joined her in all the various conferences with teachers and school administrators. He also made efforts to get to know each of Justin's teachers and showed considerable interest in reviewing with his son all the papers he brought home and the daily report forms set up by the BCBA that were used for two years. He also arranged to come with Justin and his grandmother for most of their consultation sessions with me.

Another important support for Justin was the team of teachers, the social worker, the BCBA, and the school psychologist at his middle school and at his high school. This exceptional team of educators consistently demonstrated strong interest and support for Justin. They collaborated to provide individualized support, especially in the early months when he was frequently upset and walked out of class. At such times they allowed him to go directly to his counselor, social worker, or the school psychologist, whichever was available to see him briefly, to help him identify the problem prompting his meltdown and to help him get himself settled so he could get back to class without excessive delay. They also provided frequent emails to his grandmother and father to let them know not only when there had been an upsetting incident, but also to report significant episodes of progress.

That team of educators was helped considerably by the BCBA consultant who had assisted them to gain more understanding of Justin's problematic behaviors in school and then to develop a strategy for school staff to use together to improve his coping skills while reducing the more problematic behaviors. A BCBA is a board-certified behavior analyst, usually a person with a master's degree in education or psychology, who has undergone an intensive course of study to learn how to observe behavior in settings such as a classroom or playground, to identify antecedents for problematic behavior, and then design specific behavior interventions to increase appropriate behaviors and diminish problematic behaviors. BCBAs often work with children or adolescents on the autism spectrum to help teachers and/or parents to develop and utilize more effective interventions to improve the individual's coping strategies.

One example of the interventions designed by the BCBA assisting Justin's school staff was development of a "daily report card" which identified 4 specific positive behaviors to replace his previous 4 problematic behaviors such as ripping up papers when he had made a mistake or hitting himself in the head with his 3 ring binder when he was upset. An important feature of this daily report card (DRC) was its emphasis on noting use of positive coping strategies, rather than focusing on negative behaviors.

Another useful feature of the DRC was its report on behavior over four different segments of the school day so that if Justin messed up and did not use the prescribed coping skills early in the day, it did not ruin his report for the entire day; he still had other segments of the day where he could earn positive points for appropriate behaviors. Each daily report card was then taken home by Justin to show his parents and his grandmother who would recognize and reward signs of progress while not fussing at him over segments where he had not followed the recommended strategies.

Behavioral interventions for Justin were also supported by his taking medication. Despite the initial resistance of this father and grandmother to medication, they were willing to try the medications I recommended to their pediatrician. The initial trial of guanfacine-ER at the minimal dose of just 1 mg daily helped only slightly, but it became quite effective when we gradually increased the dose to just 3 mg daily. Later we added a very small dose of methylphenidate (Ritalin). Guanfacine-ER is usually effective in reducing restlessness and emotional dysregulation, but it is not usually as effective in improving focus and ability to sustain effort.

Usually the combination of guanfacine-ER and a stimulant works quite well for many with ADHD and Asperger syndrome, although it is always important with these patients to start low and go slow in trials of medication. Many with the combination of ADHD and Asperger syndrome have a very sensitive body chemistry—bigger doses or quick dose increases are often not better.

This story of Justin includes a good example of how early adolescents with ADHD and/or Asperger syndrome often struggle with conflicting feelings about sexuality. Usually they are curious about their own sexual development and that of others, as are most others of comparable age. Yet because those with this combination of syndromes often are very limited in their exposure to peer conversations about sexuality and adults rarely provide much help in understanding sexuality, they often have little understanding of how others their age actually experience and understand their own sexuality and that of others.

Many of these adolescents just keep quiet about their sexual interests and experiences. My experience is that usually these patients are very appreciative when a parent or counselor provides information about such matters. Two books which may be helpful for counselors or parents to consult and possibly provide to some of these adolescents are *Making Sense of Sex* by Sarah Attwood (2008) which is straightforward and well-illustrated. Another helpful book more specifically focused on adolescents or adults with Asperger syndrome is Isabelle Hénault's *Asperger's Syndrome and Sexuality: From Adolescence through Adulthood* (Hénault, 2006), which offers a structured program for education about sexuality.

An important influence on Justin's future possibilities was the decision raised while he was in eighth grade. "Should he should enroll in the vocational-technical high school or the general high school which offered a college prep curriculum?" The two teachers who told Justin that he should choose to go to the vocational-technical high school did not know Justin very well and were not very familiar with his strengths. They simply thought it would be easier for Justin to learn a trade than to pursue a college prep curriculum. For some students that more technical, vocationally oriented program would certainly be very appropriate and a better fit, but that is not where Justin's abilities and ambitions were focused. For Justin, their suggestion was demoralizing and unwarranted.

Fortunately, other school staff more familiar with Justin's strengths encouraged him to pursue his interests in the college prep option and helped him to understand that his currently demonstrated abilities for academic work were just as strong as many other students in his class who would be attending the general high school. It is important for students like Justin and their families to get realistic feedback to guide their planning. It can be very difficult if they are given unrealistic hope which is likely to lead to defeat. But it is also important for them to get encouragement that will nurture their hope and ambitions for realistic striving which is not beyond their capabilities.

One additional event worthy of notice is Justin's reaction to overhearing his grandmother discussing his grandfather's cancer and upcoming surgery. Unlike what many other kids would do in such a situation, which would be to ask for more information about what is likely to happen and sharing their worry, Justin did not mention his intense fears about his grandfather, and potentially his grandmother dying soon. He went on with his daily routine, but became increasingly unable to sustain his usual performance in schoolwork and activities. Only when I pressed him during therapy about possible reasons for his declining work was he able to mention his fears about his grandparents that had been affecting him for several weeks. This is an example of how some with Asperger syndrome have considerable difficulty in processing emotions which, in many others of similar age, would have been explicitly mentioned almost immediately so they could get more understanding of the situation and more emotional support.

Part III
Young Adults

7   Anthony

I was doing really well since I came home from that out-of-state college last year. My grades in this local college are not perfect, but they're pretty good. I was feeling proud that I finally found a girlfriend and went out with her a couple of times. Then suddenly she broke it off and didn't want to see me. After that I texted and tried a bunch of times to see her, but she just said no and she got a restraining order against me. Then I met her in the college parking lot just so I could ask her what happened. I had no idea that I would get arrested and put in jail for that.

When Anthony came with his parents for an initial consultation with me he was sixteen years old. His mother gave me a report of a psychological evaluation of Anthony had undergone eight years earlier when he was in second grade. In that report the psychologist had noted:

[Anthony's parents] were concerned about his distractibility in school and wondered whether Anthony suffers from ADHD or whether he is intellectually gifted and bored in school … They described him as always different from the average child. He cries easily in school without clear cause and has always been terrified of loud noise … He has not made any friends and does not seem bothered by his lack of friendship … He will not join team sports … and won't participate in games at parties … He is afraid of Halloween, will read only non-fiction books, and loves routines, but has difficulties with transitions. While his parents feel he has few interests, those he does have he goes into 500%. His conversations often remain on the same topic and things get stuck in his mind.

In describing Anthony's responses to standardized IQ and academic achievement tests, the psychologist reported that what impressed her most about Anthony was "how markedly demanding he was of himself and his strong need to impress me with his skills or knowledge." She also noted that Anthony had a catastrophic reaction when he was unable to perform to the level he wished. He broke into tears at several points when he felt he could not perform a particular item on the test.

DOI: 10.4324/9781003141976-11

Despite his anxiety about the testing, Anthony's performance on the IQ test was in the superior range for visual spatial organization, in the high average range for verbal comprehension and in the average range for working memory and processing speed. His achievement levels for reading were in the superior range at the 96th percentile for his age while his math was in the high average range at the 79th percentile and his composite score for written expression was in the superior range at the 91st percentile.

That psychologist noted that Anthony demonstrated some characteristics of ADHD, some of Asperger syndrome, and some of anxiety disorder, but she did not feel that Anthony fully met diagnostic criteria for any disorder. She made some suggestions for accommodations in the classroom, but, unfortunately she did not recommend or provide any treatment for Anthony's multiple impairments.

At the outset of Anthony's initial consultation with me his mother also gave me some notes she had recently written to describe his strengths and difficulties:

> In some ways Anthony has been an easy child to parent. He is very sweet and kind. He is not a demanding person. Other parents and teachers always rave about what a nice young man he is and find him very interesting and unique. It always seemed he could learn things easily. He has an incredible memory and is great with trivia facts. He wants to become an engineer, but even in this area that he loves and in which he excels, his inability to work on things prior to deadlines is now creating problems for him.

In describing Anthony's difficulties early in eleventh grade, his mother mentioned:

> He has no organizational skills and his homework is now a marathon, taking twice as long as his teachers say it should. He has no sense of how to break up a long-term assignment. He only works on something if it is due … Writing is excruciating. He is often unable to start; he is afraid it will be wrong before he even starts. It is so painful for him to write that he tries to use as few words as possible … He is always told that he has good ideas but does not put enough detail in his writing.
>
> In dealing with other people he will often say things that are slightly inappropriate or that don't fit. He often misses nonverbal cues. Sometimes he is viewed as annoying because of this. Recently Anthony is becoming so overwhelmed that he just shuts down.

In these two paragraphs written prior to our first consultation, Anthony's mother described his ADHD impairments as well as characteristics of Asperger syndrome. Notably, she did not report his having patterns of overtly oppositional behavior and she clearly showed appreciation for his many strengths. However, in this note and in our initial conversation she made it clear that she was feeling very frustrated and quite worried about Anthony's current functioning and about his future in finishing high school and in preparing for college.

At the outset of his initial consultation, before getting information from his parents, I asked Anthony what he hoped we might work on that could be helpful to him. He responded:

> I'm not the most organized person, especially in my schoolwork. I have a lot of difficulty with writing papers and organizing what I want to say. That's always terribly slow for me. I'm good with factoids, but in English I'm really weak on interpreting feelings or understanding themes in novels. My grades right now are a mix of B's and C's; my only A is in Honors Physics. I used to get really good grades, but now I really struggle with my homework for 5 or 6 hours most nights, although a lot of that time is spent circling the airport. Often I'm late with assignments. I'm worried about whether I'll be able to get into the kind of college or university I want and need to become a successful engineer.

To assess strengths and weaknesses of Anthony's current cognitive functioning I administered a battery of IQ and academic achievement tests. On the Wechsler Adult Intelligence Scale–IV he scored in the superior range for visual-spatial reasoning, better than 96% of his age mates, almost identical to his testing at age 8 years; this is a significant strength for someone who wants to learn to be an engineer.

In the new testing, Anthony's score for verbal comprehension improved from the high average to the superior range, stronger than 84% of his peers. However, his score for working memory dropped into the low average range, worse than 77% of his peers. He scored even lower, worse than 96% of his peers, on a brief story memory task we utilize in our evaluations (Kennedy et al., 2016).

This pattern of relatively high scores for verbal comprehension and/or visual spatial processing with relatively low working memory and/or processing speed scores is quite common in high IQ adolescents and adults with ADHD (Brown, Reichel, and Quinlan, 2009). Many students with high IQ tend to do better on verbal comprehension or perceptual reasoning portions of the IQ test, but have more difficulties with short-term working memory or processing speed which are aspects of executive function important for deploying their cognitive abilities.

After that comprehensive evaluation, it was clear that Anthony was a very bright and appealing adolescent who fully met diagnostic criteria for ADHD of the combined type. He also was experiencing considerable anxiety. I arranged with his pediatrician to begin a trial of stimulant medication to which we soon added a trial of fluoxetine, an SSRI, to alleviate his excessive anxiety.

Within a few weeks Anthony reported that he was feeling less anxious, much better focused, and was working more productively on his homework. He and his parents returned to see me for a few follow-up sessions after which they terminated his treatment. Once his medications were stabilized, his grades had improved considerably and he felt much better. For the rest of high school Anthony was followed by his pediatrician who was prescribing and monitoring his medications. He then went away from home to enroll in a very competitive out-of-state engineering school.

Often parents assume that if their son or daughter with ADHD has a good response to treatment with medication, then all that is needed is for them to see that the prescription is regularly refilled and that the medication is taken as ordered. Often they do not realize or accept the idea that some continuing psychological treatment may also be needed for success.

My next contact with Anthony was almost two years later during his Christmas vacation in the middle of his sophomore year at the engineering school. He reported that he really liked the school, but had felt increasingly overwhelmed because he could not keep up with the heavy homework demands. He had decided to withdraw from that school and continue his studies in a local university while living at home. He told me that at that school he had continued to take the medications that had been so helpful to him in high school, but, despite this, he had felt quite anxious and somewhat irritable.

In describing his experience at that college Anthony reported that his daily routine involved going to bed at 10:30 p.m. most nights and then getting up at 4 am every morning to do his homework. He mentioned that he had not made many friends at the college and that he spent most of his time outside of classes alone. His grade point average was below 2.0 and he had lost 20 pounds over his 1 ½ years at the school.

After coming home Anthony enrolled in a local community college to take some courses for the spring term after which he hoped to enroll in a nearby university with a strong engineering program. We agreed that he would now undertake psychotherapy with me so we could better understand why his initial college experience had not worked out. We also agreed to collaborate to find ways to help him manage his work more effectively in the new setting.

As we spent time together for psychotherapy and talked a bit more about Anthony's experiences living away from home at his initial university, it became quite clear that he was suffering not only from the previously diagnosed ADHD and intense social anxiety, but also from Asperger syndrome, as had been considered, but not diagnosed by the psychologist who evaluated him in second grade. He described how he very much wanted to get to know other students in his dorm, but felt very awkward and "out of it" in social situations where everyone else seemed relaxed and joking around. He "didn't get" much of their joking and often couldn't tell whether others were teasing him or not. When I administered the Social Responsiveness Scale to Anthony and got responses about him from his family, he scored in the autism spectrum range by both self-report and family reports. This led to our continuing discussion about Asperger syndrome and how it had impacted him in both past and present.

While living at home and taking courses in a community college for the spring semester Anthony continued in weekly psychotherapy sessions. We discussed strategies for him to study and how he might recruit two or three students in each of his classes to join in a study group for that course where they would all read the full assignments with each one taking particular responsibility for a share of the material assigned. Then they would meet and each participant would take the lead in quizzing the others about his assigned section while the group combined opinions to get a best answer. With some coaching he found study partners in each of his three classes. By the end of that semester he reported:

> It's so much better doing review for exams in those study groups, much better than just staring at my own notes or the textbook for hours. Talking about it together and arguing about which would be the best answers helps me get the information into my head in a way that can stick. It also helps me get to know some other kids in my classes.

Anthony was admitted to a local university with a good reputation for its engineering program. He resumed his engineering studies at the start of the fall term.

In the course of his ongoing psychotherapy it became clear that Anthony suffered some obsessive compulsive symptoms that he had not mentioned in his earlier brief treatment. He reported that he had perseverative ruminations where he couldn't get his mind off particular worries or disturbing thoughts. He also had longstanding compulsive behaviors such as having to go up any stairway two steps at a time while counting each stair as he went and having to return to the bottom and start over if he became distracted and lost count. He reported that he had felt ashamed of these irrational symptoms and could not bring himself to mention them to me until he had gotten to know me better.

Obsessive compulsive disorder is often not disclosed early in treatment by adolescents or adults. They tend to be embarrassed about their inability to control such thoughts, especially if the content is sexual or aggressive. Prevalence of OCD in the general population is estimated to be less than 3% among children or adults. It is sometimes apparent in early childhood where the child has recurrent disturbing images of being abandoned by parents or having a family member or themselves kidnapped, injured or killed. For some, onset of OCD symptoms does not appear until late teens or early twenties (Geller and Brown, 2009). OCD is much more prevalent among adults with Asperger syndrome, often at 25%.

Another source of shame for Anthony was his lack of experience in dating or any sexual activity with a partner. Gradually he began to speak of how difficult it had been for him in high school where he often heard other boys talking about their dating exploits. He very much wanted to find a girl whom he could get to know, ask out on dates, and with whom he eventually might gain some sexual experience. "I felt like a hopeless and immature nerd." This was a domain where his social anxiety was intense.

One day Anthony came for his therapy session smiling as he announced that he had finally found a girl to be his first girlfriend. "She's good-looking and also very smart and a good student." Two weeks later he announced with much enthusiasm that he had studied with her in the school library after which they went out to get a slice of pizza. He bragged, "We're now officially going out together!"

Three weeks later Anthony arrived for his therapy session looking very dejected and complaining that his girlfriend had told him that she didn't want to see him anymore. He had pressed her for an explanation of what had gone wrong, why she wanted to cut him off. All she would say was that she saw him as a nice guy, but not someone she wanted to go out with anymore. Anthony had no idea of why she had decided to end the relationship when he had been feeling that it was going very well. He had an urgent need to find out what had gone wrong.

His friends had urged him to back off from the girl and not to try to press her for any further explanation. He was unable to stop himself. He waited for her after some of her classes, but she refused to talk with him. He tried texting her several times daily with urgent requests to meet with him just one more time so he could explain to her how he felt and why he believed the relationship could eventually work. She did not respond, and he became increasingly obsessed with his need to have at least one final conversation with her. He could not understand why she was frightened and angry about his persistently bothering her.

After a few weeks of feeling harassed by Anthony, the girl filed a complaint with the university and then with the police. That led to a school directive for him to avoid contact with her and then to a court-issued restraining order. He avoided her for a few days and then, ignoring warnings from both of his friends, from his family, and from me, he approached her in the school parking lot to make one more appeal for a chance to talk. She complained to the police. Anthony was arrested, taken to jail, and charged with stalking in the second degree.

Anthony's parents bailed him out of jail and arranged for him to be represented by an attorney who asked that I provide a note to the prosecutor explaining that Anthony suffers from Asperger syndrome and OCD. When the case was heard in court, the prosecutor took Anthony's disability into account and agreed to recommend that the judge put Anthony on probation for six months with the stipulation that he had to continue his treatment with me. The judge accepted that recommendation, but warned Anthony that if there were any further offences of this type, the penalty would be more severe.

Anthony complied with the probation requirement and gradually began to realize how his determined efforts to press the girl for more interaction had annoyed and then frightened her. He vowed that he would never resume his efforts to contact her. Yet he continued to suffer from perseverative obsessional ruminations about what went wrong with that relationship, what he could have done better. We decided to add a small dose of Abilify, an antipsychotic medication, to help him reduce the intensity of his ruminations about his ex-girlfriend. With that support he was able gradually to refocus his life so he could get his schoolwork done while he continued in his psychotherapy to address his OCD and his difficulties in understanding other people.

Reflections on Anthony and Beyond

Anthony's persistent obsession with that young woman was fueled by his difficulty in understanding that she was seeing the brief relationship with him in a very different way than he understood it. This is an example of a problem found in many individuals with Asperger syndrome. They often have difficulty in what is called "theory of mind," which refers to the ability to recognize that another person may have a very different understanding of a situation than is held by oneself.

In 1995 Simon Baron-Cohen published a book called *Mindblindness*, in which he described how autistic children tend to be much slower in understanding something that most typically developing children learn much earlier—they have difficulty in understanding that other persons may have a different idea about something than they themselves.

Baron-Cohen demonstrated this in a very simple experiment called the Sally-Anne Test done with young children 3–4 years old. A child (call him James) is in a room with two other children. He watches as Sally places a marble in a small basket on a table and then she leaves the room. While Sally is out of the room, Anne moves that marble out of the basket and puts it into a small box on that same table. James is then asked, "Where will Sally look for the marble when she comes back in?" Or "Where does Sally think the marble is?" Seeing this, most typically developing children by age 3–4 years old will correctly respond that Sally will look for the marble in the basket where she left it.

Most autistic children of similar age say that Sally will look in the box for the marble. They assume that Sally will look in the box because that is where they know the marble is. They do not recognize that because she was not in the room to see the marble moved, she does not have the same information about that marble that they do.

The difficulty Anthony had in understanding why that young woman wanted to end her very brief relationship with him was due to his inability to understand that she saw him and that relationship in a very different way than he did. He saw himself as simply seeking a brief conversation with her to find out about what had gone awry in their relationship. He did not understand that his persistent inability to accept her refusal to see him led her increasingly to see him as a stubborn nuisance and eventually as a potentially dangerous threat. He did not grasp that Sally had not seen the marble moved. He assumed that she saw the situation as he did.

In his comment the week prior to his arrest, Anthony saw that his intense need to talk with the girl was more intense and persistent than most others would experience:

> I'm realizing that often people don't understand me. I repeatedly think about the same things. Like right now I can't stop thinking about what I might have done wrong with her or what I didn't do that turned her off. I think about that during my classes and when I'm trying to do my

homework and when I'm trying to go to sleep. Most people don't feel it's necessary to keep thinking that way. But I just have to find a definite answer even if there is no definite answer!

This comment shows Anthony's recognition of the unusual intensity and persistence of his need to "get a definite answer," but it does not show any sense of how her refusal to talk with him might reflect puzzlement or frustration or fear of him on her part. He sensed his compulsive perseveration, his inability to let go. But he could not see his failure to grasp her view of the situation. He could not put himself in her shoes. More information about Baron-Cohen's view of autism and theory of mind is included in Chapter 15 of this book.

From his earliest years Anthony had a significant problem with how he viewed himself. The psychologist who evaluated him at age 8 had commented on "how markedly demanding Anthony was of himself" and "how he had a catastrophic reaction when he was unable to perform to the level he wished. He broke into tears when he felt he could not perform a particular item on the test."

These were aspects of Anthony's OCD. Often people refer to themselves or others as having OCD because they are particularly orderly in the way they arrange things or in their need to clean their home or car more thoroughly than most others do. However, there are some individuals who genuinely suffer because of the intensity and persistence of their obsessional worries and their compulsive striving for perfection. They struggle against persistent preoccupation with a felt need to do things "just so" and strong feelings of inadequacy when they are not able consistently to meet their own high, often unreasonable expectations for themselves.

In addition to his OCD, Anthony also struggled with Asperger syndrome. This was apparent when he described his self-isolation and rigid avoidance of engagement with other students at the university. Living away from home was very difficult for him, but he stuck with it for 1½ years, despite considerable loneliness and fear. He spoke of how he hesitated to join other students in his dorm each day when they left together to go to meals. He usually ate alone in the cafeteria for most meals and went to bed quite early most nights, avoiding the times when students often interact at the end of their day. He usually did his homework alone in his room in early hours of the morning rather than in the library in the afternoon or evening where most other students did much of their studying.

Throughout this period he did not report to his parents that he was struggling in campus life nor that he was having difficulty keeping up with his academic work. He felt defeated and ashamed when he finally asked to return home at the end of his third semester in that distant college. He had wanted very much to make a success of it.

Some reading this description of Anthony's struggles with his wishes to be successful in that university away from home and with his wishes to get a girlfriend might say that he should have simply resigned himself to staying at home and attending the local university that had a good engineering department, that he should not have gotten involved in efforts to begin dating. Yet what Anthony's story illustrates is that he was not satisfied to attend university close to home, he wanted to go away to school where he would live away from home and be very proud of his university. Likewise, he was not satisfied to miss out on the dating and sexual experiences that many of his high school classmates were engaged in. Having Asperger syndrome does not mean that one may not aspire to accomplishments similar to those with whom he had grown up and with whom he had attended advanced classes in high school.

Fortunately Anthony was able to use the stress and shock of his arrest as an occasion to become much more fully involved in his psychotherapy and in gradually developing his ability to take more fully into account how others may perceive various situations in very different ways than he himself viewed those same situations. The process went slowly, but it was productive.

8 Drew

My son is supposed to graduate from his university in 3 months. Last semester he did well in 3 courses, but he failed one required for graduation. Now he is taking that course again, but is failing for not attending classes. He acknowledges that he has Asperger's and ADHD, but he's skipping classes and refuses to engage in treatment.

Before 24-year-old Drew came for an initial consultation at our clinic his mother sent me a lengthy note to provide some background for their visit. She wrote that in early childhood he had been a very active and restless child who often refused to follow directions at home. He was an excellent student until fourth grade, when the teacher began to send home notes saying he was uncooperative in group activities and took too many bathroom breaks. One day that year he walked out of his classroom without permission, left the school, and began running laps around the nearby football field. When staff brought him to the principal's office he hid under a desk and defiantly told the principal that if she punished him, he would kill himself. Soon he retracted that threat, but from that time his pattern of ignoring rules, often not following directions and frequently being overtly oppositional continued in school as well as at home.

His mother reported that while in middle school Drew missed his school bus most days, depending on his parents to drive him to school. He regularly refused to shower, would not do homework, and was often oppositional with the tutor who came to help him at home, rolling around on the floor rather than doing productive work. She noted that Drew was recognized by his teachers as very bright, but he seemed oblivious to the attitudes and feelings of other children and adults. He tended to miss social cues and often took others' words quite literally, unable to recognize the significance of non-verbal expressions or the emotions of others that were easily recognized by classmates.

According to his mother, Drew tended to be a loner in high school. During his junior year he participated in a mock trial. Because he felt the group was too disorganized, he appointed himself the leader and felt he was quite successful in getting the group to prepare for the mock trial. However, when he walked into the prep room on the day of the regional competition, the entire team refused to talk to him. He reacted with hurt and bitterness. Throughout high school he spent much of his

DOI: 10.4324/9781003141976-12

free time alone playing video games and trying to teach himself to do computer coding. He had strong interest in computer science and actively used online resources to develop proficiency in programming with Java script, HTML, and Python. He graduated from high school with a cumulative GPA of 3.8 and was admitted to a reasonably competitive university.

During his sophomore year of college Drew joined a fraternity. He became intensely involved in the group's activities and tried to engineer a coup to place himself as chairman for a major project. His approach was so heavy-handed that he was voted out of the fraternity in a crushing defeat that left him resentful and severely depressed. At the end of that year, he transferred to another university on the other side of the country.

In the summer after his first year at the new university, Drew returned home and did a three-month internship for a database company where he was recognized as an extremely skilled coder who was able to hyperfocus on his work and quickly complete projects. He clearly had an aptitude for that work. His employers reported that he was solving complex data analytic projects which would be challenging to computer science majors with a master's degree.

Near the end of that summer, as he prepared to return to the university, Drew had an auto accident which was clearly the result of his being inattentive. No one was injured, but his car was totaled. His parents sought consultation from a psychiatrist who prescribed Zoloft to try to alleviate his frequent depressive episodes, but that doctor did not address Drew's chronic inattention or his social difficulties.

After returning to the university he saw another doctor who recognized that, in addition to chronic depression, Drew also suffered from ADHD. He was started on Adderall, which helped him to focus better on his schoolwork. While on the Adderall and Zoloft Drew not only kept up with his classes and assignments, he also worked a side job for a startup company where he worked long hours doing data analytics and impressed the owners with his math and computer skills.

By mid-year the startup company was failing so he lost that job. He became demoralized and tried to cope with his disappointment by smoking marijuana several times each day. His grades plummeted, which resulted in his once again becoming severely depressed, often unable to get out of bed to attend classes or to do homework for days in a row. He stopped taking the Zoloft and the Adderall and lost all his credits for that term. During that period he was involved in two additional motor vehicle accidents due to his inattention and slow reaction time. No one was seriously injured, but in each instance, the family car he was driving was totaled. Despite these difficulties, Drew did not resume use of his medications.

Drew's parents were unable to persuade him to resume his medications or to get himself into treatment. They bought him a pickup truck, hoping that the new vehicle would lift his depression. Drew took the pickup truck and went on a prolonged solo road trip through the southern states of the U.S. For 2 months he slept each night in his truck parked in various Walmart parking lots. He spent most days driving or in public libraries playing video games, stopping every few days at a Planet Fitness to take a shower. His mother commented in her letter that Drew "liked living in his truck, having all his belongings with him at all times, being able to take off from one spot to another, without having much social interaction with anyone. Discomfort of being too hot, too cold, or too humid kept him moving from one location to another." Although worried about him, his parents continued to allow him to use their credit card to pay for gas, meals and supplies. When he returned home almost three months later, his mother made the appointment to bring him to our clinic for an initial consultation.

When Drew and his mother arrived, I asked him how he had decided to come to see me. He responded, "I have difficulty getting myself to do things I'm not interested in. I get interested only in novel, complex things." He reported that he had slept through many of his classes in both universities he had attended. He said he liked programming and data analysis, but not much else. He announced that most professors were quite boring and did not teach about anything that he did not already know or that he was actually interested in. Without being asked, he confessed that he had cheated a lot in many classes, often copying from others' test papers.

When I asked Drew how his friends or fellow students might describe him he said "very smart, eccentric, does weird things, likes to do most things by himself, but a good person." He said that he did not have many friends, but that his own description of himself included the following:

> I can function only if I have all my stuff in my truck … I always need to sleep in my sleeping bag … I want to have a van and live in it … I always have to wait until I have the feeling to do something, can't do it just because someone expects it or tells me to do it. I feel like an animal, not really in control of myself.

When I asked his mother to describe Drew she responded with "very argumentative, very bright and widely read, one who dominates every conversation, and one who is quite rigid, has a lot of difficulty changing his mind, and also has a lot of difficulty in reading other people." Drew made little eye contact during this conversation and came across with a somewhat arrogant tone.

When asked about his family, Drew mentioned that his father had died suddenly of a heart attack at age 57 while Drew was in high school. His mother had not mentioned this loss in her letter. He added that his father's sudden death was not much of a surprise because his father was "severely obese, quite depressed and was often irritable and verbally abusive to his wife" (Drew's mother). He said he himself had a long fuse with most people, except for his mother, who often irritated him. Only half joking, Drew described his mother as the CEO of a large company who had retired early so she could annoy him. He described his stepfather as a recently retired software engineer who did not really want Drew around because he claimed that Drew often caused arguments.

As I described the impairments associated with ADHD, I paused periodically to ask Drew to tell me how much the various symptoms I described were true or not true of him. He told me:

I can focus on how a system works and how to probe the system, but then after I figure out how it works, I lose interest in it … I have trouble with organizing my stuff and my time and my work … I have some difficulty falling asleep sometimes and always have a lot of trouble waking up and getting out of bed … I get pissed off easily, often about little stuff … I have a good long-term memory, especially for computer data, but my short-term memory is not very good.

Drew was right about his short-term working memory. On our standardized story memory test (Kennedy et al., 2016) this very bright young man scored at the 2nd percentile, worse than 98% of same-age peers, far below what would be expected for someone whose verbal ability is in the high average to superior range. He could recall only 12 of 25 word units immediately after hearing each of the two stories. In contrast, he scored in the middle of the average range for recall of numbers forward and backward.

To assess Drew's social communication and social functioning, I administered the Social Responsiveness Scale (SRS-2) to him and asked his mother to rate him on that scale independently. Drew's responses regarding social awareness, social cognition, social communication, social motivation, and restricted interests and behavior yielded a summary score which placed him in the moderate range, a level which indicates "deficiencies in reciprocal social behavior that are clinically significant and lead to substantial interference with everyday social interactions. Such scores are typical for individuals with autism spectrum disorders of moderate severity." His mother's responses placed Drew in the severe range, which is characterized by "severe and enduring interference with everyday social interactions."

When I asked Drew about his current social relationships and friendships, he said:

I have little to no interest in small talk, learning the interests or hobbies of others, or in developing a romantic relationship. He stated, I don't care even if I can see how they're feeling, but I'm sure there are times when I completely misread how someone is feeling.

In concluding our initial consultation I told Drew and his mother that he was clearly a very bright young man with exceptionally strong skills in computer science and data analysis who was suffering from severe ADHD and persistent depressive disorder with some intermittent episodes of major depression. I also mentioned that he demonstrated problems in social communication and interaction that fit the profile of Asperger syndrome. I noted that it is certainly not necessary for everyone to be intensively social, but it seemed clear that Drew's difficulties with social communication had caused him significant difficulties in doing some things he wanted to do, for example in the college fraternity. I mentioned that such difficulties can also interfere with relationships with professors and classmates in university as well as with potential employers.

Drew had told me that he wanted to return to resume classes in the university he had most recently attended. I urged him to resume taking the Zoloft he had been taking to alleviate his depressive symptom; I emphasized that such medications need to be taken daily to be effective. I also recommended that he resume taking medication for ADHD, suggesting that he might benefit from trying Vyvanse daily with the option of a booster dose of short-acting amphetamine in late afternoon. I indicated that our clinic would be available to help in fine-tuning those ADHD medications.

In addition to the medications, I made two other recommendations:

1   I urged Drew to take at least one, preferably two, summer school or online courses over the course of the summer so that he could regain some of the credits he had lost in his last semester at the university. Successfully doing that could allow Drew to demonstrate to himself and his mother that he was ready to return to the university.
2   I advised that pills alone would not be sufficient to prepare Drew to return to the university. I recommended that Drew engage in a course of psychotherapy to address problems in organization and prioritizing his work and to identify strategies that might help him to improve his social relationships with others. I offered to see him in person for psychotherapy over the course of the summer before he returned to his university to resume his studies. If and when he returned to the university, I suggested that he seek a therapist someplace near his university who could work with him directly face-to-face on a regular basis, though I also indicated that we could continue to meet via Zoom while he sought another clinician.

Drew declared that he wanted to return to the university for the coming fall semester and agreed that he was willing to accept my recommendations and treatment. One week later Drew returned for his first psychotherapy session. He reported that he had resumed the Zoloft at the previous dose and also started with a low dose of Vyvanse as I had suggested. He reported that even with the low initial dose of Vyvanse he felt some improvement in his alertness and in his ability to work. He also had begun an online course in computer science that he found interesting. We agreed that he would try an increase in his Vyvanse dose to 20 mg each morning.

Two weeks later Drew returned for his next psychotherapy session. He reported no adverse effects from the medication and noted that he was getting more productive activity into his days and was keeping up with assignments for his online data science course. He reported that he had been getting up at 6 a.m. and was continuing to be productive with reduced time spent playing video games each day. His mother sent a note indicating that after one week of "honeymoon success" Drew's productivity declined, though it had improved again after he started the 20 mg dose of Vyvanse.

Drew did not return for an additional therapy session for the next six weeks. He then made an appointment and came in reporting that his prescriber had increased his Vyvanse in two steps up to 40 mg which was consistent with what we had initially projected. He said he had experienced some excessive sweating at this higher dose, but he did not consider this a big problem. Drew also proudly announced that he had successfully completed the data science course he had undertaken and that he was now working on a new project to plan and monitor his daily goals for himself. Buoyed by this success, Drew was planning to move back to the university if he was granted readmission. He said that his mother had previously purchased a house near that campus that she had been using as a rental property. She had told Drew that he could have a room in that house if he was able to return. I suggested that it would probably be helpful if Drew came to see me regularly so we could work together more effectively to monitor his progress and to help him prepare for resuming his university studies.

After another interval of six weeks, Drew returned for another psychother-apy session. He had received word from the university that he would be allowed to return for the fall semester. His mother had arranged for him to have a room in her rental property and she was planning to live in another room in that house to provide him support for his returning semester. I expressed some questions about whether mother and son living in such close proximity at that time might undermine Drew's ability to function on his own. I felt that the relationship between them was so volatile that eruptions of conflict would be likely. However, both of them were convinced that the arrangement would be workable.

I also told them that the wide intervals between our therapy sessions were leaving us with no time to adequately address Drew's social communication problems. I mentioned to both Drew and his mother that we could do some sessions by Zoom if the two-hour drive to my clinic was problematic; they said they would consider that option.

Neither Drew nor his mother contacted me until seven weeks later. When they arrived for their appointment, eight weeks after the previous session, they announced that they were both moving to their home near the university one week later. At that time Drew had registered for five courses which, if suc-cessfully completed, would leave him with just one more course to complete his degree. We discussed factors essential to his success in the upcoming semester. He spoke about how he realized that consistent class attendance and consistent use of his medication as prescribed would be critical.

When she came in at the end of the session his mother said that she wanted to add another critical factor, that Drew should get into bed each night by 9 p.m. so he would be able to get up for his morning classes. I suggested that she not get into trying to manage such details of Drew's life since he was now 25 years old and needed to take responsibility for managing his own daily routines. I predicted that if she got into trying to control details like bedtime, it would lead to conflict and undermine Drew's taking responsibility for himself.

Two weeks after his classes began Drew had a Zoom session with me. He repor-ted that his classes were going well so far, except for one. He noted that he was unhappy with that one of his five courses because the professor was very smart, but not a good teacher. I suggested that he might consult with another student in the class or go to see the professor during office hours to see if he could get some additional help with the course. Drew responded that such actions would be useless, that he would not even listen to the lectures, that he would try to learn the course content on his own. I encouraged him to talk with his designated academic advisor. In the last few minutes of our Zoom session Drew reported that he had met a girl that he liked to hang out with. He said "we don't call each other a couple, but we are friends and we do date type activities." He seemed happy about this.

On the day of that Zoom session I received an email from his mother saying that so far Drew had been going to his classes and was actually doing his homework. She also reported that Drew had finally read the book on Asperger syndrome that I had recommended to him. He told her that he had decided that he actually had Asperger syndrome. She proposed sending Drew to attend social skills workshop "to help people like him in learning social skills and communication manners." She also asked if I thought treatment with neurofeedback might be helpful for her son.

I told her that I did not think neurofeedback would be at all helpful and that she ought to avoid trying to push him to join social skills groups. I encouraged her simply to support Drew's efforts to do his job as a student and encourage him to either maintain close contact with me by Zoom or to begin work with a psychologist or psychiatrist near the campus with whom he could get the ongoing treatment he needed.

Drew had another Zoom session with me a couple of weeks later. In that session he reported that he had dropped one course and planned to take it in the next semester. He said that his other four courses were going well. He said that he was attending all of his remaining classes regularly and thought he was doing reasonably well in all of them. He also mentioned that he was feeling frustrated with his mother entering his room when he was out. He said that he did not want her entering his room when he was not present. I told him that I considered that a reasonable request so he could have some privacy and suggested that he try to explain that to his mother. That was my last direct contact with him. I had no further contact from Drew or his mother over the next four months. Neither responded to several emails I sent asking how things were going and encouraging them to get back in touch.

Early in the second semester, Drew's mother wrote me the following email:

> I am still living with Drew in my rental home near the university. First semester he registered for five classes and didn't like the teacher in one, so he dropped that one early. In three courses he did quite well on his grades, but he failed the other which is one he needs to graduate. That failed course is actually about computer work he had very successful experience with in both of his previous internships; he should have no technical difficulty in learning the subject matter. The problem is his social and interpersonal behaviors.

At the beginning of fall semester Drew positioned himself as the only smart student in the class; he said all the others were dumb and useless while the professor was incoherent and unable to teach. He said other students asked him to tutor them ... On the mid-term he thought he got everything right and finished early. He got 40 out of 100! After the mid-term he was totally humiliated, deflated and cut off all contacts with his classmates. At the end of the semester he said that the professor had told the class what kind of problems would be on the final and that he knew it all, so he didn't need to study for the final. Despite my encouraging him to study, he did not. He failed the final exam and failed the course ...

In the last 10 years I have witnessed half a dozen spectacular failures in Drew's life, all follow the same pattern and this is the latest one. He is now enrolled again in that class he needs to make up—it looks like he will fail this course again. If so, he will be one course short of graduating from college and he will have no college degree, no job, no income, and will probably make himself homeless again.

Years ago Drew recognized his head was not right and he was determined to find out how to fix it. He recognized he was depressed and we got that treated with medicine. He still had problems and you helped him recognize and get treatment for his ADHD. Then you explained his having Asperger syndrome and started to work with him on it, but he was not willing to continue with treatment. I read the book on Asperger syndrome and it explained everything that had gone wrong with Drew over the past 10 years. This semester will be over in 3 months. What can you do to help him?

Mother and son were both on the other side of the country. I immediately wrote both of them offering to talk with them by Zoom. I also suggested that they go the student health services at the university to get immediate help. I have had no further word from mother or son.

Reflections on Drew and Beyond

To this day, I do not know how Drew and his mother are doing. However, regardless of their outcome, this case example illustrates the frustrating and sometimes tragic consequences that can come to an individual with Asperger syndrome and his family if they do not receive adequate diagnosis and obtain consistent treatment when the child's impairments become apparent. Drew's difficulties were not evident in his preschool years, but signs of his impairments began to emerge in the middle of his elementary school years. More serious problems in interpersonal relationships were quite evident in middle school and in high school even before the sudden death of his father.

One important factor was the unwillingness or inability of Drew's parents to confront his arrogant and defiant attitude toward them, school staff, and others. They continued to praise his strong intelligence and accomplishments, but they did not challenge his ignoring rules or impose consequences for his repeatedly expressing contempt for classmates and teachers. Nor did they insist that he participate in getting an evaluation and treatment when negative behaviors persisted.

Likewise, they imposed no consequences for his careless driving. After he totally wrecked two cars, they provided new cars without delay. Even after his wrecking a third car, they did not withhold driving privileges or insist upon his using medication prescribed for his ADHD. They bought him a new pickup truck and allowed him to use their credit card to support his almost three-month-long road trip.

Sometimes parents feel that there is nothing they can do to impose negative consequences when their young adult children are careless in driving or unwilling to meet reasonable expectations such as attending school and doing their schoolwork or finding and keeping a job. However, consequences such as limiting access to driving family vehicles, withholding spending money and use of a credit card until reasonable responses are forthcoming may serve to teach the important lesson that failure to fulfill responsibilities can lead to unwanted consequences.

His mother brought Drew to our clinic for treatment, but neither mother nor son could sustain sessions consistently enough for the treatment to have adequate impact. Mother and son both ignored my recommendations for more frequent sessions, leaving excessively wide intervals between therapy sessions, thus undermining progress. Hopefully, at some future time each of them will be able to sustain treatment to help them interrupt their repeated pattern of conflict so that Drew can utilize his impressive potential.

9 Sandra

> I've attended three different colleges and have lots of credits, but I haven't been able to complete a college degree. I have a lot of trouble completing any essays or term papers because I'm a perfectionist. I give too many details and have to get each sentence to sound "just right" before I can start writing the next sentence. Often I just can't get the papers done. I don't know how other kids do it because I don't really get to know anybody else. I love animals more than I like people.

"I'm supposed to be really bright, but though I've spent 6 years in full-time study at three different colleges and have lots of credits, I still don't have my bachelor's degree. The main problem is that I struggle with writing essays and term papers." Twenty-five-year-old Sandra introduced herself with those two sentences when she came with her mother for an initial consultation with me. They reported that Sandra had been recognized by her third grade teacher as having attention problems. She had a trial of Ritalin, but this was discontinued after a couple of months because the dose prescribed made her feel too anxious.

No further medication treatment was provided for her ADHD, but in fourth grade through middle school Sandra earned very good grades and did quite well on standardized testing. She was identified as a talented and gifted student. She told me that she loved to learn, but hated school during elementary and middle school years. She said "I didn't feel that I fit in well. I tried to be friendly, but I hated spending seven hours a day with people who didn't really know me."

Sandra reported that it was during high school that she had first encountered significant difficulty with written expression. This was noted in the report of a psychological evaluation she had undergone when she was 17 years old. After administering a battery of IQ and achievement tests, that psychologist noted that Sandra tended to be overinclusive in her writing, which leads her to become bogged down with less important details. She has difficulty selecting the most important relevant information and moving forward. She referred to this as being too perfectionistic in her writing.

When I asked Sandra about her family, she told me that she had felt very close to her mother until she was about 13 years old, but from that time on

DOI: 10.4324/9781003141976-13

she had more mixed feelings toward her mother who had become very moody, quick to anger and pretty depressed. She described her father as a very intelligent man who was "very bright but also very depressed, a master of ignoring things." She noted that while she was a freshman in high school her father was diagnosed with cancer and had to spend a month in an intensive care unit for complications.

In describing her family and social relationships, Sandra mentioned "I don't like to feel strong emotions, so I never let anyone get emotionally close to me." I asked if she spent any time with one or two friends, a group of friends, or did a lot of things by herself. She responded, "I'm kind of reserved in relationships with friends, but I've had a boyfriend for four years, though he's in college on the other side of the country and we rarely have any contact with each other."

When I asked Sandra how she might be described by classmates or others who know her, she said "super smart, but probably too rational, often late, gets very passionate about the environment and equal rights, I don't blow up, but I can get easily annoyed, pretty sarcastic and scathing." Sandra described a situation during her sophomore year of high school where she had confronted a girl about being unkind to another girl. That incident had led to all of Sandra's friends siding with the girl she had confronted and "dumping me." After telling about this incident Sandra told me: "Girls are catty and will dump you."

I asked Sandra what she was hoping to do for work when she completed her college degree. She responded quickly, "I want to be a vet tech because I like animals more than I like people." This attitude about interpersonal relationships was alluded to in a psychological evaluation Sandra had undergone four years prior to her consultation with me. That psychologist had noted:

> Although she can appear to be comfortable in more superficial relationships, Sandra struggles with considerable social discomfort and a tendency to avoid getting close to others … She reported that she dressed all in black in the "goth" style during most of her high school years and that other kids in high school tended to see her as smarter than themselves.

Yet the report of that psychological evaluation also reported that Sandra told her psychologist "I feel ridiculously stupid compared to my family. All of them are brilliant and we make fun of stupid people."

Sandra also reported to that psychologist that she engaged in episodes of cutting herself during high school "because feeling pain was better than nothing which is what I had been feeling, but it was not because I wanted to kill myself."

The psychologist also reported that Sandra often avoided attending classes near the end of her senior year in high school. Sandra told the psychologist that she did not really deserve to graduate with her class because she had missed so many tests for her math course. Her math teacher had helped her re-take all the math tests so she would be able to graduate.

One possible reason for Sandra's avoidance of classes near the end of her senior year of high school might have been her being afraid to move away from home to enter the college she had selected to attend which was located more than a thousand miles from her home. Sandra reported to me that she did not like change and that during her freshman year at that college she felt miserable because she had a frustrating roommate and was so far away from home.

During high school Sandra began to see a psychotherapist for depression and anxiety which she thought were fueled by her persistent feeling of not fitting in with her classmates. At that time she took Effexor, an anti-depressant that was prescribed to help alleviate her depressive feelings and anxiety.

In her psychological evaluation done at age 17 Sandra reported high levels of worry and intrusive thoughts related to social issues at school. At that time she had also reported chronic difficulties in organizing her work and materials, in getting sufficiently activated to start, sustain efforts and complete assignments on time which were not recognized as aspects of ADHD.

Psychological testing in that evaluation indicated that Sandra's abilities in verbal comprehension on the WAIS IQ test were in the very superior range, stronger than 99% of her age mates while her perceptual-organizational abilities were slightly lower, though in the superior range. However, Sandra's scores on achievement testing for reading, writing and math were generally quite a bit lower, in the average to high average range. On the timed essay writing test she obtained a much lower score. She told the examining psychologist, "I started out OK, but I got caught up in proving my point and being perfectionistic. I couldn't be concise. I didn't plan well at the beginning and so I wasn't able to finish within the time limit."

In our interview I asked Sandra to tell me a about her experience when writing an essay or term paper. She described how she had always tended to struggle with making decisions—whether what to choose from a restaurant menu or what facts and ideas would be most relevant for an essay she was writing. She would try to consider all information that might be even remotely relevant while jotting down notes to help her remember all the possibilities. Often she felt stuck in that information gathering stage and had very limited time to prioritize and decide on how to organize and sequence what she was trying to talk about.

Sandra told me that she had always felt a need to get things organized and complete. She mentioned that she keeps all the books on her Kindle alphabetized by author names and that when putting lights on the Christmas tree she felt a perfectionistic need to get each light placed "just right" to form a consistent pattern. She also felt a need to arrange clothes in her closet and her dresser sorted by their season and then by their dominant color groupings.

I asked if Sandra was able to write a first draft of an essay or term paper and then go back to reread and edit it to create the final draft. She said she was never able to do that because she feels a need to get each sentence perfectly worded before she can move on to write the next sentence, only then can she move on to write the next sentence. Then, at the next sentence she once again had to get the words to look and sound "just right" before she can move on the write the following sentence. This rigid perfectionistic approach to writing is often seen in persons with obsessive compulsive disorder.

Trying to get each sentence to look and sound perfect before the next sentence can be written is an exceedingly slow way to complete writing tasks. Typically, those who suffer with this version of OCD are well aware of the fact that their way of writing is irrational: typically, they are neither stupid nor crazy. Yet they feel a strong compulsion fully to comply with their felt-need to proceed in this way, even though they may see and recognize that the compulsion is not rational.

The psychologist who administered the second psychological evaluation for Sandra described her approach to the essay writing as "she became bogged down in her desire to be overly inclusive and subsequently was not able to finish her essay within the allotted time." While it is unlikely that Sandra actually desired to be "overly inclusive" in her essay, it is likely that she felt a need to be very thorough, not excluding any information that might help the reader to understand fully what she was trying to explain. The net effect of this, apparently, was her being overly inclusive and unable to finish the assignment in time.

The problem of "over-inclusiveness" in writing is not uncommon among persons with ADHD. It might be compared to the problems seen in many adults with ADHD who make daily "to do" lists that include every task they can think of that they want to get done, often this list will include 20 to 30 tasks for completion that day, far more than any mortal could possibly complete is less than a month. They have great difficulty in selecting and assigning priorities as to what needs to be done now and what needs to be put off for another day or may not need to be done at all.

A related aspect of this difficulty in writing is a problem with setting levels of abstraction. Many bright individuals garner many ideas or much data to include in what they want to write. But they get confused about how to assign priorities to sort out which are the key points they want to highlight, which are subordinate points, and which are less significant details that may be interesting, but don't need to be included at all. They have great difficulty in moving repeatedly in their thinking from the macro view of the task to the micro view and back again. They tend to get stuck in looking at a few specific trees while not keeping actively in mind the forest in which each of those trees is just one part.

In my evaluation of Sandra, I asked her to write a brief essay in just 10 minutes within which she would say what is her favorite game and then to explain three reasons why she likes it. On this task she offered many interesting ideas, but her essay was weak on structure and coherence. It also lacked a wrap-up summary or conclusion. Despite knowing that she had only 10 minutes in which to write the essay, she never listed the three reasons she liked that game. Her writing wandered off into stating interesting facts about the game, but never really explained her reasons for liking it. This took so much of her time that she was unable to write a concluding paragraph or even a concluding sentence.

In discussing this problem after the testing, Sandra and her mother both commented that family members often complain of similar problems in conversation with Sandra's father. They often feel that he gives excessive details in what he says, so much that the main point of what he is trying to say or explain is very difficult to discern. Characteristics of OCD, like those of ADHD, tend to be quite heritable.

At the time of her evaluation with me Sandra had been taking for several years large doses of two antidepressants, Cymbalta and Wellbutrin-XL, neither of which is recommended for treatment of OCD, a diagnosis which had not been recognized in any of her three previous evaluations. I suggested that her prescriber might consider reducing or discontinuing one of the current antidepressants and instead prescribe for a trial of one of the SSRI medications approved for treatment of OCD.

Sandra was also taking a moderate daily dose of Vyvanse for ADHD which had previously been diagnosed. She said that the Vyvanse was somewhat helpful for both attention and improving her mood and alertness. I suggested that her prescriber might consider a trial of an increased dose of Vyvanse to see if that might be more effective. If not, another option that might be considered would be augmenting the Vyvanse with morning and mid-afternoon doses of short-acting dextroamphetamine which might improve activation, especially in the morning when Vyvanse is slow to kick in.

I also emphasized to Sandra and her mother that medication alone was not likely to be sufficient for adequately dealing with Sandra's combined difficulties with written expression, ADHD, social anxiety and obsessive compulsive disorder. I told them that I did not see in Sandra at this time any evidence of generalized anxiety disorder, but I did see that she had significant problems with Social Anxiety, which is excessive worry about how she is perceived or likely to be perceived by others, coupled with a tendency toward avoidance of close social interactions or intimacy. To address these issues I suggested that she undertake some psychotherapy to focus on her social anxiety, OCD and her difficulties in reading others' emotions.

To assist Sandra with her problem in written expression I suggested that she might seek a writing tutor who could work with her through the various elements of organizing and integrating her thoughts to make them more understandable to others. I suggested that a good writing tutor might be able to help Sandra alleviate her excessive perfectionism and her tendency to be overinclusive in her writing. However, I also suggested that she might want to select courses for completion of her undergraduate degree that did not involve substantial writing requirements. If she intended eventually to work as a veterinary technician it was likely that some additional courses in science might be more useful to prepare her for work in the veterinary field.

Reflections on Sandra and Beyond

Of all the persons described in case studies of this book, Sandra is the least likely to be seen as having Asperger syndrome. In some ways she seemed interested in others and in having relationships, so long as the relationship did not become very intimate. In her contradictory patterns of relationships Sandra clearly qualified for the diagnosis of social anxiety disorder. She also met diagnostic criteria for obsessive compulsive disorder, and, as noted earlier, for ADHD. While many with Asperger syndrome do have both social anxiety and OCD, most do not have the level of apparent interest in relating to others which reportedly seemed apparent sometimes in Sandra.

There are several ways in which Sandra seemed quite different from most people with Asperger syndrome. One difference is that Sandra's mother reported that there were no problems in Sandra's early social development. She described Sandra in early childhood as one who cooperated readily and shared well. She said that Sandra made friends easily and was generally viewed as a leader among her peers. Another difference is illustrated in that the psychologist who evaluated Sandra at age 17 wrote that "Sandra is keenly aware of other people, watches them carefully, and is adept at sensing what they want and need."

That psychologist also noted:

> I found Sandra to be immensely likeable. She is bright and engaging … She is accustomed to being viewed by others, and often experiences herself, as a "bubbly, gentle caretaker, who tries very hard to keep other people happy" … Reportedly everyone likes the fact that she seems to be a kind and gentle friend.

These characteristics are quite different from those usually found in those with Asperger syndrome.

Yet each of Sandra's several psychological evaluators noted that while Sandra was appealing and reported social interactions with others during the periods described, she also seemed to keep from engaging in closer friendships and more emotionally intimate relationships. The same psychologist who mentioned that he found Sandra "immensely likeable" also noted:

> there is a discrepancy between how easily Sandra seems to relate, on the one hand, and her resistance to genuine connections on the other … the nature of her underlying connections seems tenuous. She will appear to be involved, but actually holds back and generally relates in a very cautious, emotionally distant manner.

The psychologist who evaluated Sandra four years later made similar observations. She wrote:

> Sandra is clearly interested in others … however she also struggles with a great deal of social discomfort and a tendency to avoid getting close to others. She tends to keep others at a distance because she feels socially inadequate and does not know how to interact with others in a more emotionally vulnerable relationship, although she can appear to be comfortable in more superficial relationships … to protect herself she keeps others at a distance, yet this leads to social isolation …

In her interviews with me Sandra herself described and gave an example of these difficulties, as was reported earlier in this chapter:

> I'm kind of reserved in relationships with friends, but I've had a boyfriend for four years, though he's in college on the other side of the country and we rarely have any contact with each other.

That statement about being "reserved in relationships with friends" and having a boyfriend on the other side of the country with whom she rarely had any contact could be seen as a way Sandra presented herself as having a more intimate type of relationship while also keeping herself at a very safe distance emotionally as well as geographically.

This is an example of what some writers about autism in females refer to as "camouflaging," making deliberate efforts to mask or compensate for their autism traits. By saying that she has a boyfriend who is far away, Sandra could appear to be having an emotional relationship with a boy as many other girls her age do, and, at the same time, avoid a relationship with a boy that might be more uncomfortable for her, for example, sexual activity.

In my conversation with her about her earlier school years Sandra reported that she loved to learn, but "hated school" during elementary and middle school years because "I didn't feel that I fit in well. I tried to be friendly, but I hated spending seven hours a day with people who didn't really know me." She told me that her persistent feeling of not fitting in with her classmates during high school led to depression and anxiety which caused her to begin taking antidepressant medication and to begin treatment with a psychotherapist. Her emphatic statement that she "hated" spending school days with "people who didn't really know me" was a strong expression of emotional distance that she did not seem anxious to bridge. Her dressing in Goth costume through most of her high school years was another way of keeping her distance from her classmates.

Also striking was Sandra's statement "I want to be a vet tech because I like animals more than I like people." Temple Grandin, one of the women on the autism/Asperger spectrum whose writings are included in Chapter 1 of this book, has written extensively about her feelings of closeness to animals. She developed her career on her ability to empathize with animals as they show many characteristics seen in autism. Her book *Animals in Translation* (Grandin and Johnson, 2005) elaborates on these connections. Sandra's statement that she "likes animals more than I like people" might be seen as a both a statement of her difficulty in feeling comfortable with other people and her more secure comfort in relating to animals where emotions can be expressed and experienced without the complexities that often arise in human social interactions, especially during adolescence and early adulthood.

During her high school years Sandra had volunteered to work at an animal rescue shelter. She spoke about how she enjoyed helping to care for the animals, exercising, feeding, bathing, and brushing them. She mentioned with pride how she especially enjoyed talking to and interacting those animals who responded to her care with signs of affection.

It appeared that Sandra was quite cut off from much of her emotional life. The psychologist who described Sandra's episodes of cutting herself quoted Sandra as telling her that the pain she felt from those episodes of cutting herself "was better than nothing, which is what I had been feeling." Sandra added in that comment that the cutting "was not that I wanted to kill myself." Apparently, the self-cutting at that time was a way of briefly immersing herself in emotion from which she was usually detached, at least in that period of her life.

There was one time, however, when Sandra did make a suicide attempt by taking an overdose of prescription medications in the medicine cabinet at her home. It occurred after an incident where she was arguing with her supervisor for her work at the animal rescue shelter. He raised his voice to her and she responded by raising her voice to him, after which she quit. Later that night she took an overdose of prescription medication thinking that her life would no longer be satisfying because she had now cut herself off from the contacts with animals that were a major source of satisfaction in her life. After doing this she decided to tell her mother so she could get the needed medical attention and live.

In concluding my consultation with Sandra and her mother I encouraged them to focus on getting Sandra help with the impairments in written expression that were interfering with her completing her undergraduate degree and constituted her stated reason for seeking consultation. I also explained that it would make sense for her to get medications and some psychotherapy to address her symptoms of ADHD and OCD, both of which were contributing to her difficulties in writing and to her social anxiety. I mentioned in the process she might want eventually to work with the therapist to consider the role that Asperger syndrome might be playing in her frequent difficulties interacting with others.

A few days after my consultation with Sandra, I received an email from her mother:

> Sandra may write you to ask for this herself, but she is still very confused about your assessment of the brief essay she wrote about Scrabble, her favorite game. She feels she answered that question. She's also stinging at being compared to her father, so that clouds the matter.

The prompt for that essay was to write for just 10 minutes saying what is your favorite game and then state three reasons why you like it. In my wrap-up meeting with Sandra and her mother I had explained that her essay was interesting, but it did not say anything about why Scrabble is her favorite. It did not mention any reasons why she liked it. She had simply described the game and many details about how it is played. That resulted in her getting a lowered score, despite the fact that she included some interesting facts about the game. Her mother mentioned at that time that Sandra's father often is known in the family for not getting to the point. Apparently, the mother had forgotten that it was she who brought that up.

I was surprised to find in that email that Sandra was still upset about my critique of her essay. The fact that her mother wrote me to ask for elaboration in Sandra's behalf was also interesting as well as unusual. I felt that the note suggested an interesting bond between mother and daughter as well as Sandra's hypersensitivity to criticism which apparently was not challenged by her mother.

10 Jorge

> My son has come a long way since he was first diagnosed with ADHD and Asperger syndrome 14 years ago. At that time he was clearly bright, but was extremely immature in so many ways. Yesterday he graduated as the top student in the computer science department of his university and he already has a job in his field. He has needed a lot of support, and still has significant problems to work out, but his future is now looking more hopeful.

His parents were separated when they brought eight-year-old Jorge for an initial evaluation with me. They were preparing for a divorce and wanted my report to assist in working out custody arrangements. Both parents emphasized their pride in their only child who had scored in the very superior range on an IQ test administered to him one year earlier. The psychologist who did that testing wrote:

> Jorge is a boy of very superior overall intellectual functioning … who experiences significant sensory integration difficulties and also shows signs of having difficulties with social interactions, and a limited appreciation of skills needed for effective social relationships.

Jorge had been born seven weeks early, weighing 4 lb 10 oz; for his first two weeks post-delivery he required a ventilator and oxygen. Since then he had developed well except for multiple allergies and the fact that he was still struggling to get adequate control over his elimination; he was diagnosed with daytime enuresis and encopresis, and still had "accidents" at least twice daily, but not during the night.

When we first met, Jorge was living with his mother and had always been home-schooled by her. He spent each weekend with his father. He participated in music lessons and various small group enrichment activities with other home-schooled children, but he had never been enrolled in any regular school for classroom activities.

When I interviewed Jorge with his mother he was very slow to respond to my questions. He needed considerable prompting from his mother to answer simple questions about what activities he enjoyed for fun and what he was

DOI: 10.4324/9781003141976-14

currently working on for his home school studies. In describing his participation in home schooling studies his mother noted that he performed well in every academic subject "so long as you keep it interesting to him."

When his mother spoke for him about his music classes, Bible class and other enrichment activities Jorge would acknowledge what she said and sometimes elaborated on it, but overall he was much less responsive than would be expected of such a bright child. He seemed to have considerable difficulty staying engaged in the conversation.

When interviewed with his father, Jorge gave very sparse answers to questions, just as he did with his mother. He acknowledged that when with his father, only with his father, he often had play dates or sleepovers with other boys whom he knew from his music classes. His father reported that Jorge never initiated efforts to invite a friend over to play, but that he did seem to want and enjoy those activities when they were arranged for him.

Jorge's father said he was very worried about his son's immaturity, not only in his inability to manage his elimination in an age-appropriate way, but also because Jorge was unable to do many other things that normally would be done by a boy his age, for example, being able to cross a street safely, to acknowledge truthfully when he has misbehaved or made a mistake, and to play a board game without having to cheat.

The clinical psychologist who had evaluated Jorge one year prior to my evaluation had described him as follows:

> a very attractive, well-developed 8-year-old boy who is quite curious and imaginative ... He struggles with attention and concentration difficulties, particularly with tasks that are more challenging for him such as written language and fine motor tasks. He appears to focus intensively on one task at a time and has difficulty switching cognitive set or turning his attention to simultaneous internal or external cues. He relates more easily to adults that to peers ... His difficulties in social-emotional and self-care skills interfere with his participation in group activities, peer relations, and a regular classroom situation.

That psychologist diagnosed Jorge as having ADHD, predominantly inattentive type with enuresis and encopresis.

To assess his current levels of academic achievement in reading, math, and written expression I administered the WIAT-II achievement test to Jorge. His scores in reading and math exceeded those of 99% of his age mates. His score for written expression was in the average range, weaker than 55% of his peers. This relative weakness in written expression is not surprising. Many bright students with ADHD have difficulty with written expression because the process of putting thoughts into sentences and paragraphs involves greater demands on executive functions than does reading. Berninger and Richards have described how "writing requires more work on the part of executive processes than reading does":

Control processes for reading are not as taxing as the executive processes that go into generating ideas and setting goals, translating those ideas into text, transcribing that text, and reviewing and revising it and repairing a text until … it is a final product in writing.

(Berninger and Richards, 2007, pp. 174, 187)

Throughout his testing with me Jorge demonstrated chronic attention and concentration difficulties. He often spaced out after he was asked a question; at such times he tended to remain inattentive until I explicitly called him back to the task. Many questions needed to be repeated to Jorge because he was not attending fully enough when the question was initially asked. This occurred not only on more complex tasks, but also on very straightforward tasks such as defining one word at a time for the vocabulary subtest. He was also extremely slow in giving his responses to questions, much more so than is common for most children his age. Jorge's composite scores on the tests did not adequately reflect his actual abilities, but clearly displayed his chronic and severe inattention problems.

My diagnostic impression of Jorge in that evaluation was in agreement with the previous psychologist regarding his having severe ADHD as well as persisting difficulty with daytime enuresis and encopresis. I also diagnosed him as having Asperger syndrome. My primary recommendation was that Jorge should be given an adequate trial of treatment with appropriate medication to try to alleviate his severe ADHD impairments. I also noted that such medication treatment with stimulants might help Jorge to be able to exercise more adequate control over his persisting problems with his toileting. I recommended extended-release Adderall with a booster dose of immediate release to help with homework in the afternoon.

While both parents agreed that Jorge had significant impairments related to ADHD, they disagreed over my recommendation for a trial of medication to alleviate his ADHD. His mother strongly opposed treatment with any medication because she felt it would be likely to blunt his emotions and dramatically change his personality. Her resistance to medication treatment persisted despite her being given factual information to the contrary by myself and two other experienced medical mental health professionals involved in assessing and caring for Jorge.

Because Jorge's father favored Jorge getting a trial of medication treatment, the bitterly contested matter was referred to the attorney who had been appointed by the court to represent Jorge. Ultimately the matter was taken before the judge dealing with the parental divorce. The judge required that the medication trial be implemented and ordered the mother to cooperate in administering the medication to Jorge as prescribed by his pediatrician. Soon the medication trial produced positive results that were noticed not only by Jorge and his father; eventually his mother too agreed that the medication was helpful and had not produced the adverse effects she had feared. By that time Jorge had fully resolved his enuresis and encopresis. Resolution of the divorce equalized the amount of time Jorge spent with each of his parents every week, though his mother continued to homeschool him until he completed seventh grade.

Jorge was then enrolled in eighth grade at a small private school. After successfully completing that year he enrolled in ninth grade at a nearby private college-preparatory school which offered small classes and strong support for students. There he did quite well academically for four years. He enjoyed playing percussion instruments in the school's band while also participating in the robotics club. During those years Jorge was being followed by a local psychologist and local physician while having intermittent Skype psychotherapy sessions with me. He and his father continued to fly in for us to have occasional face-to-face follow-up sessions.

When he was 17 years old Jorge came with his father for a re-evaluation with me. At that time they were beginning to think about what plans might be appropriate for Jorge after he graduated from high school. Testing with the WAIS-IV indicated that Jorge still scored in the superior range, at the 95th percentile, for verbal comprehension and working memory while his score for visual spatial reasoning was in the average range and his score for processing speed was in the low average range. Academic achievement measures from the WIAT-III showed that he was functioning in the superior range for math, written expression, and oral language; his reading comprehension score was near the bottom of the average range.

At that time Jorge had already successfully completed a couple of AP courses and was doing reasonably well in all of his academic courses with the support of daily sessions with a private tutor and the accommodation of extended time for taking tests; the accommodation was to compensate for his slow processing speed. All his grades at the time were A's. Comments from his teachers included:

- "Jorge has a quick, nimble mind; he easily makes connections between general rules of nature and specific physical events."
- "His math abilities are first rate; he has made a very good start in Calculus."
- "Jorge excelled in all aspects of Microeconomics … his graphs were not very neat, but they were accurate."
- "What Jorge offers in English class is apt, clever, and deepens understanding of all of us for the subject at hand. Likewise, his writing shows increasing sophistication in development."

To assess Jorge's strengths and difficulties in social interaction, I asked Jorge, his parents, his tutor and two of his teachers to complete the Social Responsiveness Scale (SRS-2). Results clearly indicated that Jorge demonstrated persistent difficulties with social cognition, social communication, and restricted interests. Result were summarized as showing "deficiencies in reciprocal social behavior that are clinically significant and lead to substantial interference with everyday social interactions. Such scores are typical for those with autism spectrum disorders of moderate severity." I also asked Jorge independently to rate himself on the SRS-2. Results were identical to those from his father and teachers. His honesty and self-awareness were impressive.

By that time Jorge had gradually distanced himself considerably from his mother. He felt that she was overcontrolling and intrusive. He still maintained regular contact with her, but their interaction was more minimal than is typical of most adolescents at that age. His interaction with his father was more frequent, but was primarily around planning and reminders of tasks to be done. Jorge rarely showed any overt affection to either of his parents. Though he remained quite dependent on them in many ways.

At the conclusion of that evaluation, Jorge and his parents asked me to prepare a list of concerns for them to consider in planning for Jorge to go to college. My response began with a general statement about the impressive progress Jorge had made over recent years in his schooling and academic growth. Then I suggested the following concerns for them to consider as they planned for his post-secondary education:

1   To do his schoolwork, Jorge is currently much more dependent upon intensive daily support from his parents, his tutor, and his teachers than are most students his age. He apparently needs intensive support to keep track of assignments and to organize his time and work. For tasks in which he has strong personal interest Jorge can work intensively and productively, but he still requires considerable adult encouragement and persistent pressure to start and complete tasks that do not presently interest him.

2   Jorge has improved somewhat in his ability to interact with peers, but most of his peer interaction is within the structure of very small classes in his present school where most classes include only 8 or a maximum of 17 students. He does not seem motivated to engage socially with peers outside the structure of school or other adult-organized activities. Even in adult supervised activities such as group discussion at school, Jorge reportedly is impatient or condescending, sometimes coming across as intolerably arrogant.

3   When not engaged in structured activities supervised by adults, Jorge tends to immerse himself in playing video games. He enjoys this activity, but he needs regulation from his parents to prevent him from spending excessive time in gaming and insufficient time in doing schoolwork.

4   Jorge is currently taking several medications which are very important for supporting his adaptive functioning and health. His father has expressed concern about whether Jorge is motivated to take these medications as needed without someone living with him to remind him.

5   Jorge reportedly has much difficulty in making transitions from one activity to another, especially if he is engaged in an activity he enjoys. It seems likely that, if living in an unsupervised situation he would have considerable difficulty in getting himself regularly to classes.

6   One of Jorge's current motivations in school is making an effort to please his teachers so he will get favorable feedback. In most post-secondary school settings classes are much larger than in Jorge's present school so there is less opportunity to get personalized attention at all comparable to what is currently motivating Jorge.

7   Jorge's father has told him that in order to go to any school where he would be living away from his parents, he would need to demonstrate readiness over the course of a year by: (a) getting all his homework turned in on time; (b) managing his personal hygiene adequately (e.g. daily showers, deodorant, etc.); and (c) adequately managing his daily healthcare and medications (e.g. for ADHD and digestive system). When discussing these stipulations during his consultation with me, Jorge explicitly stated that he is uncertain of his ability to meet those minimal requirements.

8   Jorge has considerable difficulty in adjusting his attitudes and behavior to the expectations of other people. He tends to view many situations in terms of only his own point of view and seems to have considerable difficulty in taking sufficiently into account the views, needs and demands of others, including teachers and classmates.

All of these concerns can be problematic for most students moving away from home to attend college or university. They are stated here because there is considerable evidence that, despite his progress, Jorge is much more vulnerable than most of his age mates to these potential difficulties that could severely disrupt his functioning in college life.

After considering these concerns, Jorge and his parents decided that they would try to arrange for his father to relocate to live near to whatever university Jorge was going to attend so he could provide a place for Jorge to live with parental support, at least for his first year of undergraduate work. Jorge fully accepted that plan with a slight show of relief. Fortunately, his father's employment allowed him to relocate and work remotely with only occasional brief travels.

Before Jorge graduated from high school, his high grades and scores on the SAT brought him offers of acceptance from several universities that had strong departments of computer science, the field he wanted to enter. He accepted an offer from a university with an exceptionally strong computer science program. Soon his father made arrangements to rent housing in the distant city where that university was located.

Meanwhile, Jorge was becoming increasingly anxious, moody, and irritable in anticipation of the move to college. He is a person who does not like to make changes in his routine or setting. A psychiatrist who saw Jorge for consultation at that time continued his ongoing regimen of stimulants, but also prescribed a low dose of the anti-psychotic, Abilify, to address the moodiness and intense irritability. This was quite helpful and was continued after the move. The only problem was that it caused weight gain because it stimulated Jorge's appetite considerably. Eventually the Abilify was replaced by a low dose of Latuda which, along with a diet plan, allowed Jorge to get his weight under better control.

Once settled in their new two-bedroom apartment, Jorge's father arranged to hire two young women who were graduate students in the university who were studying to become speech/language therapists. These young women were employed to come to the apartment for 2 to 3 hours on alternate days for the purpose of helping Jorge to keep himself organized in his studies, to get off to classes on time, and to maintain an adequate routine of daily self-care. They also occasionally took him grocery shopping or on other outings during which they were to help him improve his conversational skills. Jorge got along reasonably well with them and their presence also maintained support for him when his father occasionally needed to be away for business trips.

With the support of his father and the two graduate students Jorge made a very good adjustment to his studies and was rapidly recognized as an exceptionally strong student in computer science. In one of our occasional Skype therapy sessions Jorge reported to me that faculty in his department were impressed by his skills in solving problems that were often difficult for them. Over summer sessions they paid him to assist in their own projects.

Jorge tended to be quite reclusive and did little direct socializing with peers. With the help and prodding of the graduate students he was generally regular in attending his classes and usually kept up with his academic work. Most of each day, when not in class or doing assignments, he spent many hours playing video games. Except for classes, he rarely left his residence. He usually ate alone in his apartment, consuming prepared food he had ordered for delivery; only rarely would he agree to join his father for dinner. Once weekly he went out to join a group in playing Magic: The Gathering, a card-based role-playing fantasy game.

On the morning of one Father's Day, Jorge suggested to his father that he would like to go to dinner together, a pleasant surprise for his father. When his father arrived home to go to dinner, Jorge announced he had eaten a late lunch and was too full to have dinner as planned. When I discussed this with Jorge in our Skype session a few days later, he seemed oblivious to his father's disappointment. As we discussed it, Jorge recognized that his father does a lot for him and said he recognized it would be good to take his father to dinner another time soon, but he said he was uncertain about whether he would remember to do so.

In that same conversation Jorge reported that he had recently flown to a distant city with a friend to participate in a video game tournament for several days. He said he enjoyed that trip, but after a few days with his friend at the tournament he had begun to feel tired of being around other people so steadily and needed a week or two to recover from the resulting fatigue. Intensive social interaction is not easy for him, even when engaged in activities he enjoys. Quite a few persons with Asperger syndrome or have similar reactive fatigue from sustained social interaction.

Jorge graduated with honors for his undergraduate degree; he was the top-ranked student in his entire department. He and his father were both quite proud of that accomplishment and the fact that he already had a job to begin immediately after graduation. In discussing this he mentioned that he still has additional goals. He wants to earn additional certifications to become a data analyst, to work toward getting himself out of his home more often to interact with others. He also noted that he aspires to find a girl with whom he might eventually develop a relationship.

Jorge's father was anxious to help his son to prepare for his new job, his first experience in being employed. He took Jorge to buy some appropriate khaki slacks and collared shirts and to get his shaggy hair cut by a barber while also getting a shave, something Jorge rarely bothered to do for himself. He was very concerned with details such as Jorge's chronic disregard for personal hygiene such as regular use of deodorant. He also feared that Jorge's frequent disregard for arriving promptly for his classes might carry over into his often being late to work. Being a businessman, Jorge's father was very much aware of how sometimes a new employee's inattention to such details can make for a difficult beginning for a new job. Jorge responded with annoyance, finding it hard to believe that such apparently trivial matters might be considered important by people busy with software engineering.

As it turned out, Jorge earned very positive reactions from his employer for his quickly understanding the projects they were working on and making useful proposals to improve their system. However, each day when he arrived home from work he spent the rest of his time alone in his room playing video games. He ordered food to be delivered to him, ate alone, even if his father was in the apartment, and kept to himself. Occasionally he spoke to me about how he intended to go out to rejoin the group playing Magic: The Gathering he had previously attended, but he did not actually do it. He would play video games steadily from late afternoon until well past midnight. It appeared that he had little interest or energy in interacting with other people after working a full day at his job, even though his work involved mostly working at a computer and very little interaction with people, including his father living in the same apartment.

Reflections on Jorge and Beyond

It should be recognized that most families do not have the financial resources or occupational flexibility to provide the resources provided for Jorge. With the structure and support provided by his father and the part-time workers who helped him get up and out to his classes and to complete homework assignments before immersing himself each day in gaming, Jorge made very impressive gains. He not only completed his college degree, but he graduated at the top of his class and soon began a full-time job where he has been performing quite well. At present, he remains quite isolated socially, but it is not yet clear whether he will be able or willing gradually to increase his interaction with co-workers, family members, or others.

Yet what is striking in this example is Jorge's sustained distancing from his mother since his moving in with his father and his continued distancing from his father. His mother put much time and effort into home schooling and caring for Jorge from birth until eighth grade when he began spending increasing amounts of time with his father. After Jorge left to go to university there have been occasional visits and phone calls with his mother, but far less than would be typical of most college students. Jorge has not been hostile to his mother, but he demonstrates little emotional engagement with her.

Jorge's interactions with his father have been much more frequent, as they share the same apartment, but most of their interactions seem to occur as the father is reminding his son of things to be done. Never has there been much sharing of meals or shopping or watching TV together. The description earlier in this chapter of Jorge's offering to go out to dinner with his father to celebrate Father's Day and then eating a late lunch and simply telling his father that he was no longer hungry is a poignant example of Jorge's feeling some gratitude to his father for the many things he has been given, but then forgetting the gesture intended to express appreciation.

Jorge had no sense of his father's disappointment when he suddenly told him that the surprising gesture of appreciation had been forgotten and was not going to be rescheduled. This is an example of how Jorge, like many others with Asperger syndrome, is quite limited in his ability to anticipate or read emotions of others when those emotions are not explicitly expressed. For Jorge's father that experience was somewhat like the experience of a parent who smiles at an autistic infant and does not receive a smile in return. After that incident, Jorge's father said to me, "He doesn't give a damn about me. I know that. He never has, regardless of what I do for him. That's just the way it is."

In their 2002 book *A Parent's Guide to Asperger Syndrome*, Ozonoff, Dawson and McPartland observe:

> In the very remote, non-verbal children who have classic autism, reciprocity difficulties are obvious. In high functioning children and adolescents … reciprocity problems may be more subtle. Parents often describe a feeling of one-sidedness in interactions with their child. Sometimes parents feel as if they must carry the whole relationship, supporting and scaffolding the interaction to establish some meaningful connection. If they don't start the conversation or ask the specific questions, the child may have very little to say or be totally content on his own … without paying much attention to the parents or altering his or her behavior in response to what the parents say or do.
>
> (Ozonoff et al., 2002, p. 185)

Although it is easy to understand the frustration of Jorge's father in this incident (and many others), my impression from hearing Jorge's report of the situation was that it was not so much a matter of his not feeling any gratitude for his father's care of him. It seemed more that he felt some gratitude which led him to suggest going to dinner with his father in honor of Father's Day, but he was not able to recognize how important that gesture was to his father. He did not have the awareness of his father's pleasure in receiving the invitation and he certainly could not anticipate and was unable to imagine the disappointment and hurt that his father felt when the proposal was not carried out. This is an example of Simon Baron-Cohen's concept of "mindblindness," described in Chapters 7 and 15 of this book, which is characteristic of many with Asperger syndrome.

However, in such situations, it seems important to keep in mind that this problem may not be due solely to impairments of the child. Parents differ in their ability to model expression of emotion for their socially-emotionally impaired son or daughter and in their ability to help the children recognize their own emotions and emotions of those around them. Asperger syndrome is quite heritable; it tends to run in families just as does ADHD.

If a parent of a child with social-emotional impairments has some measure of such impairments himself, it is likely to be especially difficult for that parent to mentor that child over the course of childhood and adolescence about what has been called "the hidden social code" described in Chapter 16 of this book. Such parents are not to blame for inborn impairments of their children or for their own limitations in helping their child to compensate for their social emotional impairments if they themselves have inherited a measure of similar impairments.

Ozonoff, Dawson and McPartland have described how a variety of traits run in families of people with autism or Asperger syndrome, especially traits related to areas of language and social abilities:

> Higher rates of language delay, articulation problems, learning difficulties, social difficulties and social anxiety are more often found in relatives of people with autism than in family members of people with other disabilities such as Down syndrome. Studies indicate that these milder difficulties show up in 10–20% of siblings of individuals with autism and often in parents as well … The strengths of people with autism and Asperger syndrome can run in their families too. Parents and siblings often have similar talents and interests as those people with autism spectrum disorders.
>
> (Ozonoff et al., 2002, p. 67)

Those authors drew on research done by Simon Baron-Cohen (described in Chapter 15 of this book), who demonstrated that parents of children with autism or Asperger syndrome were more likely to be engineers, physicists, or mathematicians than parents of other children, and were more likely to be proficient in solving technical problems than most other parents, but also not as proficient as the other parents in some social skills like reading facial expressions.

Ozonoff and colleagues summarized the relevant genetic information on this topic in the following:

> What appears to be transmitted in the families of people with autism spectrum disorders is not an autism spectrum disorder per se, but a certain distinctive style of thinking, relating, and reacting to the world that brings with it both limitations and strengths.
>
> (Ozonoff et al., 2002, p. 68)

When trying to understand people with Asperger syndrome or other autism spectrum difficulties and their parents (or anyone else), it is important to attend not only to impairments they may have inherited and manifest, but also to the strengths that may emerge from similar sources.

Part IV

Adults

11 Richard

When I graduated at the top of my class and then got hired in a big law firm, I felt good, but they terminated me in less than a year for reasons that were never clear. Then I got a job at another law firm and got fired from there because I was late in completing a couple of projects and didn't communicate enough with my supervising partner. My girlfriend and I have lived together for several years. She says I'm smart and work really hard, but have difficulty reading where others are coming from. Now I'm looking for a new job, but it won't be easy.

When he first entered my consulting room Richard was well dressed in a business suit with tie. He was carrying an elegant leather briefcase from which he removed and handed me a formal résumé that summarized his education and his employment history. He then introduced himself by saying that he had graduated at the top of his class from a very competitive college and a very competitive law school and had passed the bar exam. Richard then looked at the floor and quietly mentioned that over the past two years he had been employed in two different law firms and had been fired from each of them before the end of his first year.

Richard mentioned that he had previously been diagnosed with ADHD and had been taking prescribed medication for it. He also told me that he believed that his failure to sustain employment in the law firms was probably due to something more than just ADHD and that he hoped I might be able to help him identify that "something more" before he tried to seek new employment.

I asked Richard how he thought his co-workers and friends might describe him. He responded:

Intense in the work environment, works hard, moves fast, sometimes impulsive, not timely, gets really invested in law projects, has a hard time ending research to complete a project, never engaged socially in the workplace, doesn't express anger at work, and has difficulty reading where others are coming from.

Richard was accompanied by Sarah, his girlfriend, with whom he had been living for several years. I asked Sarah how she would describe Richard. She responded

DOI: 10.4324/9781003141976-16

with "very smart, inconsistent, short-fused, gets agitated and irritable, but not seriously angry, sometimes forgets the point of a story, overpromises and under-delivers. Often, he's late. He was 30 minutes late to our first date."

To provide more information about himself Richard handed me a report from a psychological evaluation he had undergone ten years earlier. The report indicated that on the Wechsler Adult Intelligence Scale Richard had scored in the very superior range, at the 99th percentile for verbal comprehension. The psychologist who wrote that report noted that at that time:

> [Richard] described himself as scattered, disorganized, and forgetful. He says he tends to lose belongings, misses appointments, and forgets to pay bills. He feels that his classroom assignments are often "meaningless" and "beneath him" which he recognizes as a problem. He grew up being told by parents and teachers that he was "exceptional" and was "highly esteemed as a very intelligent person." Now he feels he is not able to accomplish anything "due to my attitude" and to his inability to sustain his efforts. He procrastinates, then feels overwhelmed and gets behind. He is able to focus "only if very interested" and, even then, he tends to take on numerous activities and is unable fully to attend to any of them.

As a result of that evaluation Richard was diagnosed with ADHD, combined type and was started on stimulant medication which he had continued to take and was still using at the time of his evaluation in our clinic.

I administered the Brown Executive Function/Attention Rating Scale to assess Richard's current level of ADHD impairments. Independent ratings from both Richard and Sarah yielded summary scores indicating significant impairment in all six clusters of executive functions associated with ADHD despite his current regimen of medication for ADHD. Further indication of ADHD impairment was evident in Richard's responses to our verbal memory test. He scored at the 16th percentile, worse than 84% of those of similar age in the normative sample. Given these indicators of significant persistent executive function impairments, it was quite impressive to know that Richard had earned very high grades in his undergraduate studies and in law school, both of which were completed in very competitive schools.

To obtain more information about Richard's social functioning I administered the Social Responsiveness Scale–2nd edition to Richard while also soliciting independent responses from Sarah to get her views of Richard's social functioning. Results from Richard's self-report scored in the moderate range which indicates "deficiencies in reciprocal social behavior that are clinically significant and lead to substantial interference with everyday social interactions."

Before sharing results from the SRS with Richard and Sarah, I asked him to describe the reasons that he had been let go from two law firms in as many years. To answer he handed me a copy of a report he had been given by one of the law firms summarizing impressions from various senior partners who had worked with and evaluated him. Reviews from the supervising partners were mixed. One wrote: "Richard is a very talented legal analyst and skilled at research and plumbing legal arguments." Another stated: "Richard is an enthusiastic and forceful writer and his commitment to his projects shows clearly on the page ... He is an enthusiastic contributor to meetings, but it would be helpful if he ... would take time to listen to others' comments."

Another partner wrote: "Richard was very eager and willing to work hard on his assignments, however, he did not take instruction or feedback well ... he was overly defensive when I explained my frustrations." Another wrote:

> Richard had a hard time meeting deadlines and often invested far more time than needed to complete tasks ... He did not utilize work others had done on the project I assigned him. He seemed to want to reinvent everything for himself ...I found those efforts not to have been useful.

Summary comments for the evaluation included:

> Several evaluators indicated that Richard should give more careful consideration to the points he is making before speaking in team meeting and he needs to listen more openly to others' comments. Some also commented that Richard did not meet some deadlines and that he was inefficient in utilizing the prior work of the team.

After reading these comments, I asked Richard if he could give me a couple of specific examples that could illustrate the supervisors' concerns. His first example illustrated his problem with recognizing his place in the social hierarchy. He told me of how when he was a junior clerk for a senior judge he expressed directly to the judge his criticism of that judge for having put a particular defendant in jail. Richard recognized that he had spoken out of turn only after he saw that the mood of the judge immediately darkened, though he made no other response to the comment.

Richard told another story of how he had been asked by a senior partner to prepare a research summary of facts and previous legal decisions relevant to a particular case. The attorney told Richard that he needed the written summary for a meeting with the client several days later. Richard worked many hours on the project up until the moment of the meeting with the client. Without letting the attorney know he would be late, Richard arrived with the summary 30 minutes after the meeting with the client had been scheduled and started. Only in retrospect could Richard recognize that he had left the attorney in an embarrassing situation with the client and that he should have contacted the attorney much earlier to get help to complete the project on time.

In further discussion of that incident Richard acknowledged that he had been so focused on getting into his summary all the information that might be relevant, that he had not at all considered how the attorney would feel about the delay, regardless of how comprehensive the summary turned out to be. In response to further questions Richard also acknowledged that he often struggled with excessive perfectionism and over inclusiveness in his writing, unable to efficiently prioritize which information was relevant and warranted inclusion versus what information was less directly relevant and should be left out.

As we concluded the initial session of Richard's consultation, I told him that he clearly met diagnostic criteria for ADHD and that his current medications did not seem to be adequately addressing those difficulties. I also mentioned that he was right in suspecting that something more than just ADHD was involved in his difficulties with the law firms. The evaluations by the supervising attorneys and his own stories indicated that sometimes he had been strikingly insensitive to the views, feelings and needs of his coworkers and supervisors in each of the firms. His own responses and those of Sarah on the SRS-2 also indicated significant problems with social reciprocity. I suggested that in addition to ADHD Richard also had been struggling with Asperger syndrome and with some features of obsessive compulsive disorder manifest in excessive perfectionism and over-inclusiveness in his writing. I briefly explained each one.

Initially Richard expressed distress about these two additional diagnoses that he had not previously heard. However, he responded thoughtfully by saying, "I want to learn more about both Asperger syndrome and OCD. Each one seems to pick up on some parts of me that I haven't really recognized before, and each one has probably affected a lot more than just my troubles with the law firms."

Before concluding that initial session we reviewed the medications that been prescribed for Richard at a previous clinic two years earlier. The doctor at that clinic had diagnosed Richard as having a mood disorder and prescribed Lamictal 200 mg. daily. My evaluation had not found evidence for a mood disorder, but because Richard reported that Lamictal had helped to improve his mood and that trials of several SSRI medications and Buproprion had caused intolerable side effects, we agreed to continue the Lamictal.

For his ADHD Richard had been taking Vyvanse 60 mg each morning and felt it helped his focus somewhat, but did not provide much benefit for his alertness. We continued the Vyvanse but augmented it with Adderall immediate release 10 mg tablets to be taken three times daily. Richard had also been taking Aripiprazole 2 mg daily to help alleviate his excessive OCD symptoms and anxiety. We continued that medication and subsequently increased the dose to 2 mg twice daily. Although our clinic was prescribing these several medications for Richard, I also told him that I thought medication alone would not be sufficient to help him address the difficulties he was struggling with. I emphasized that he would also need some psychotherapy to address his difficulties, particularly his Asperger syndrome impairments. He agreed.

In our next session Richard began by telling me that he had been thinking a lot about the Asperger diagnosis and realized that he has had those problems for a long time. He said:

> Back when I did my clerkship there were two other clerks in the same office, both of them women, who were very rigid, rule-bound

personalities. I felt they were not very bright and I never really got to know them. After I had arrived at work just 10 or 15 minutes late a few mornings they reported me to our boss, an older judge who was a stickler for timeliness. From then on, I never talked with them at all. I also didn't talk much with the judge's secretary with whom those two other clerks were often chatting.

Near the end of that clerkship I found out that the secretary had received a call from someone who was ready to hire me for a new position and was calling to ask for a reference. She didn't even let the caller speak with the judge. That secretary actually told that caller, "He doesn't get along well with other people. Don't hire him!" I guess that's a good example of how apparently minor social incidents left unresolved can do unforeseen damage.

Richard said he had also been thinking about how the Asperger syndrome might be relevant to his relationship with Sarah. He described how Sarah usually came home from her job about 6 pm feeling very hungry, yet he was not usually hungry at that time because he had eaten late lunch:

so usually we defer dinner until 7:30 p.m. or later. I was repeatedly ignoring her hunger and fatigue. And at least once a week I usually go out to eat by myself, especially if I'm feeling irritable. I haven't recognized before that I often am inconsiderate of Sarah.

Another example is that I often start reading right after dinner and then stay up reading until 2 or 3 a.m., but that means I don't spend much time interacting with Sarah in the evening before she has to go to bed so she can get up early in the morning for her job. And right now she's really supporting both of us because I don't have much income except what little I bring in by tutoring a couple of people preparing for the Law Board exam.

I told Richard that I thought he had just given a number of examples of his being so caught up in his own interests and needs that he was pretty insensitive to the needs and feelings of others, even this woman he was living with. He agreed and told me that in a book he had been reading in the past week about Asperger syndrome the author had mentioned that often those with Asperger syndrome lose relationships they have tried to make with a partner because they don't pay enough attention to the needs of their partner.

He told of an example in that book where a man with undiagnosed Asperger syndrome had been shocked when the woman he loved left him without his having any clue that there had been a problem in their relationship. Richard told me that he felt a need to improve his interactions with Sarah so he could avoid her eventually abandoning him in a similar way.

Richard began our next session by telling me that he had been thinking about what he might do to improve his relationship with Sarah. I asked what ideas he had come up with. He reported that he probably should be trying to earn some more money rather than depending upon Sarah to carry the whole financial burden of supporting the two of them. I asked what he had been contributing to expenses for Sarah and himself.

Richard explained that he had been earning some money by tutoring college students who wanted help in preparing themselves to take the LSAT or law students who wanted help in preparing to take the law board exams. However, he had wanted to take on just a couple of students for tutoring at a time because he felt he needed to reserve at least half of his time to work on his memoir while he was seeking a job. I asked how he thought Sarah felt about his carrying such a small share of their expenses while he was setting aside so much time for writing his memoir, a task usually undertaken by persons who had lived considerably longer than he had. He said that Sarah had never complained about it, but, upon reflection, he thought he probably was being unfair to Sarah. I suggested that he might want to reconsider his priorities and talk about this Sarah.

Meanwhile, I asked Richard what he had been thinking about regarding his seeking a job. He responded by saying:

> I don't know how I will ever be able to get another job in any law firm, given that I have been fired in less than a year from each of my first two jobs in a law firm. I can't avoid reporting them to any potential employer. The state regulations require that any attorney seeking employment must disclose any previous job where your employment has ended under unfavorable circumstances. That means that I probably would be seen as a high risk, even though high potential applicant.

I asked Richard what other options he was considering. He said that ultimately he hoped to be able to return to employment in a law firm. However, he felt that at present he would seek a position in a corporation where he could be engaged in legal research and also collaborate with the in-house counsel staff. After establishing a good record in such a position, he hoped he could eventually find a position in a law firm. He indicated that he was beginning to look for some such possibilities.

A few weeks later Richard reported that he had been reading a book he had found about perfectionism and how it often leads to procrastination resulting in excessively late or incomplete projects. This led to additional discussions about past experiences in the law firms where he had delved deep into research on various projects, adding more and more data and citations, many of which were excessive and were so distantly related to the topic that they were actually not relevant to the issue at hand. In doing such work it seemed that he felt a need to amass so much information that it would be very unlikely any reader could accuse him of having overlooked any potentially relevant information. Richard began to recognize how his enthusiasm for covering all possible points often interfered with his bringing projects to timely completion.

About one month later Richard reported that he had located a lead for a possible position in large corporation. He was interviewed several times and he was hired in a position that fit quite well with his interests.

As Richard began to prepare for his new full-time position we had a number of conversations about lessons he might take away from the difficulties he had experienced in his law firm jobs. We talked quite a bit about the importance of his trying to develop some social contacts among those in any firm where he might eventually be employed. I emphasized the importance of his developing and maintaining a file in which he would note brief comments about the person's name and a few details about the background and a few characteristics of each new person he met. One purpose of this exercise was to encourage him to develop the practice of greeting by name people he had met while trying to keep in mind their specific characteristics and interests, possibly developing and nurturing friendships with a few of them.

I encouraged him to make efforts from the outset to become acquainted with co-workers and supervisors in his new position. Seeking evaluative feedback from coworkers and supervisors is often needed by those with Asperger syndrome both for the benefit of improving the content and quality of their work and also for the purpose of developing some personal interaction that could reduce misunderstandings and possibly develop some friendships.

Reflections on Richard and Beyond

This story about Richard illustrates how some individuals who are highly successful in their schooling up to the point of graduation struggle in making the transition out of their long history of schooling into the very different world of seeking and sustaining employment. Several books and articles have been written about how children struggle to learn the "hidden social code" of interacting with their peers in classrooms and on playgrounds. Learning to deal with the implicit social codes of the workplace can be even more challenging.

Whether large or small, the workplace is likely to involve informal, but complex social hierarchies with co-workers, supervisors and managers of differing ages with varying levels of experience, and seniority, only some of which is likely to be explicit in the formal hierarchy of the organization. Richard learned this when he found out that two interns and the office secretary had become annoyed with him and reported his occasions of tardiness to his boss. He learned it even more painfully when he learned that the secretary had sabotaged his getting any reference from his employer to a prospective employer.

Richard's difficulty in forming relationships with more senior members of the two legal firms that eventually fired him provides examples of his struggle to recognize the need for developing relationships with more experienced colleagues and supervisors. Positive relationships with more experienced workers in a job setting is critically important whether one is starting work as a laborer on a construction site, as a salesperson in a retail store, as a lawyer in a law firm, or as a resident physician in a hospital.

In his *Seasons of a Man's Life*, Daniel Levinson described the need and complexities facing a young worker trying to develop a mentorship relationship during early stages of his career. Levinson described the multiple functions of a mentor:

> He may act as a teacher to enhance the young man's skills and intellectual development. Serving as a sponsor, he may use his influence to facilitate the young man's entry and advancement. He may be a host and guide, welcoming the initiate into a new occupational and social world, acquainting him with its values, customs, resources and cast of characters … the mentor may be an exemplar that the protégé can admire and seek to emulate. He may provide counsel and moral support in time of stress … He represents a mixture of parent and peer; he must be both and not purely either one.
>
> (Levinson, 1978, pp. 98–99)

Developing a relationship with a mentor can be extremely valuable for a young adult as he tries to establish himself in a new career, but not everyone has access to a potential mentor and, for those like Richard who persistently struggle with managing their emotions and social communication, it can be extremely difficult.

Richard's difficulties in interacting with his supervisors in the two law firms were clearly related to his chronic difficulty in noticing nonverbal communications in facial expressions, tone of voice, eye contact and his weakness in the ability to "mindread," to put himself in the shoes of supervisors and other staff and learn gradually to interpret their intentions and concerns. Those aspects of social communication and interaction tend to be very difficult for those with Asperger syndrome regardless of how proficient they may be in academic learning. Such difficulties are not usually helped by medication alone, except insofar as a medication may reduce social anxiety or impatience and impulsivity.

What is usually needed is supportive counseling or didactic psychotherapy where specific examples of problematic interactions can be reported and discussed. Such discussions need to include not simply the counselor or therapist hearing a description of interactions. What is most needed is for the therapist to demonstrate empathy for the patient in dealing with such situations while also guiding the patient to develop better understanding of the other person's likely viewpoint and concerns. Often it is also helpful for the therapist to suggest some possible strategies and tactics, perhaps even some specific wording that might be helpful in such situations. One resource for helping patients with such tasks may be adapting principles from the *Getting to Yes* by Fisher, Ury, and Patton (2011).

12 Loretta

> I graduated from a very competitive college and a competitive law school, and I passed the bar exam to become an attorney; but I've never had success in social relationships with anyone. I'm always anxious around other people at work or in social situations. I feel other people just don't get me and I don't get them. I was actually engaged to a man for four years, but I ended that relationship because he was always so frustrated with me. I'm good at my job and pretty content on my own, though I have been feeling depressed recently.

Loretta flew across the country to come for a consultation in our clinic. She explained that she had recently had her 40th birthday which stirred up in her a persisting feeling that she has been failing in life. Despite her having a prestigious job as a research attorney with a comfortable income, and despite her having graduated from a top tier college and a prestigious law school, she had long felt like a failure. This birthday had really intensified that feeling.

I asked Loretta what aspect of life she felt she had failed in. She responded:

> I feel like I've failed in the fun part, the relationships part. I'm so mired in day-to-day life that I don't do much for fun. I've always been kind of a loner, sort of reserved, off to the side. I don't feel that people get me. Or I just don't relate. I don't have many friends anymore. I'm pretty content on my own. Setting up a time to meet someone to do something socially seems arduous.

In response to her saying she does not have many friends anymore, I asked what it was like previously when she did have some friends. This led her to describe how she had been engaged several years earlier to a man named James and that she had broken up with him after they had been engaged for four years. She explained that she ended that relationship "because he was often frustrated with me after he got close enough to really see me."

I asked what James had gotten so frustrated about as he had gotten to know her better. Her initial response was puzzling. She said "Most people are more constant than I am. I've very sensitive to lighting and to temperature. Something about how I'm taking in the world." I queried, "More constant in what?" She hesitated, and then responded:

DOI: 10.4324/9781003141976-17

I guess it wasn't about lighting or temperature. He used to say that I seemed inconsistent about wanting the two of us to be close to each other. I guess he was right. I wanted to get married to him, but at the same time I didn't want to get married. I kept going back and forth. Sometimes I wanted the closeness and other times I wanted to pull away. He got frustrated with that and I just told him it would be better to end it.

At that point I suggested that Loretta focus a bit more on what she had said about her own feelings regarding closeness with James. I told her that what she was describing sounded like a civil war within herself—shifting repeatedly from wanting to have increased closeness with him and then, at other times, wanting to pull away. I asked if she could describe a bit more about how those changes actually happened.

Loretta responded by telling me not about James, but about her relationship with her first close friend who was a boy, Rick, whom she had met in her first year of high school and depended on throughout her high school years. She described Rick as one who helped her understand a lot of information in high school that she found very difficult to understand on her own.

I've showed you the report from that IQ test that was given to me when I was six years old. On that test I scored at the 99th percentile. Yet I didn't learn the same way most other kids did. That became very clear when I got into high school. Often I had no idea of what was going on! Rick was able to explain concepts to me so I would be able to understand what the teachers were talking about and what we were supposed to be learning in our classes. It took me much longer than other students to process information that was unfamiliar to me. I often needed any complex or simply unfamiliar oral or written information to be explained to me. Rick used various concepts, diagrams, pictures or associations that helped me to relate what was being taught to things I already knew and understood. He intuitively knew how to support my particular type of visual learning.

Loretta's description made it sound as though she was a foreigner in high school surrounded by teachers and other students speaking a language she could not understand—and Rick was a very bright translator who could transform the language of instruction, befuddling to her, into terms that conveyed the information in ways Loretta could fully understand.

What was not explicit, but clearly seemed implied, was that Loretta found Rick to be demonstrating not only effective translations of what she was struggling to learn. He also clearly showed consistent and convincing respect and caring for Loretta. It is likely that the intensity and persistence of this unique and intense relationship was gratifying to him as well.

Loretta denied that there was anything sexual in their relationship, but there certainly was much affection which, presumably, was reciprocal. This woman who described herself as having always been introverted apparently was able to connect, perhaps platonically, but certainly reciprocally and intensively with Rick in ways she had never been able to connect with anyone else before or since. Apparently she thrived on this relationship for all four years of high school.

Loretta graduated from high school with excellent grades, increased awareness of her cognitive strengths, and much gratitude to Rick for connecting with her and for helping her effectively to utilize her exceptional intelligence despite her learning difficulties and her ADHD impairments. That separation and loss of Rick was not easy.

When Loretta graduated from high school and headed off to a very competitive college she no longer had the presence or help of Rick. Initially she continued to suffer from the persistent problems in executive function, symptoms of ADHD, that had plagued her since early in her schooling and for which Rick's steadfast tutoring had provided an ongoing compensation.

In her college, however, Loretta soon discovered an important factor that offered her the protection she needed from her ADHD impairments. Unlike most other colleges, the curriculum of her college provided uniquely wide freedom for students to choose classes which were interesting to them. There were no constraints imposed to meet general education requirements with specific courses.

For the first time in her years of schooling Loretta was able to choose only courses in which she felt interest. She explained, "I could take courses with teachers who were really interesting and I could pick classes that were not in the morning." This was quite different from high school where she was required to take quite a few classes that held no real appeal for her. This freedom to choose all her classes based on her interest in the subject matter or the professor allowed Loretta the ideal situation for persons with ADHD.

As is described in Chapter 14 of this book, those with ADHD can usually exercise their executive functions quite well when doing tasks in which they have strong personal interest, either because of the subject matter or because of the teacher or companions sharing in the task. Evidence for this "central mystery of ADHD" was manifest in Loretta's academic work throughout almost all of her college courses.

In addition, being able to avoid taking morning classes was a boon to Loretta because she had experienced lifelong difficulties with regulating her alertness. She functioned best when she could postpone going to bed until about 4 am and then sleep until noon. In situations where she had to be up at 8 or 9 in the morning, Loretta struggled to get to sleep early and needed a sequence of four alarm clocks to awaken her.

At her college, Loretta found a wide variety of courses that were quite appealing to her, most of which started in the afternoon. This allowed her usually to work effectively late into the night and then sleep until noon so she could get sufficient sleep to function effectively for the remainder of her day. With this flexibility of choice in courses and scheduling of classes and sleep, Loretta was able to function very well throughout her four years of college.

Not only did she earn a cumulative GPA of 3.9, she also blossomed in her ability to participate in group discussions and to engage very constructively in discussions with other students and with her professors.

As she concluded her undergraduate studies, Loretta received from several professors letters showing enthusiastic support for her application to law school. One wrote:

> Loretta was in my undergraduate lecture course. She was the best student in a class of 350. More important, she showed exceptional interest in the material ... She has an original yet clear thinking perspective on society and the world of ideas. Watching her debate is a treat because one can see her intellectual and persuasive powers in action.

Another professor described Loretta as "a highly effective individual":

> When she starts out on a project she pushes through to completion and does it well. She is a woman who gets things done! ... She also excels in the classroom context. For example, in a small undergraduate seminar of only 16 hand-picked students, she clearly stood out as the best student in the class ... She has shown an extraordinary ability to challenge under-lying assumptions of assigned readings, she offers unique, insightful comments about the topic being discussed and has an impressive ability to find meaningful connections between diverse ideas, seeing things with a fresh perspective.

Loretta's high grades in college and impressive recommendations from her professors won her admission to an excellent law school. However, in our consultation as she described her difficulties in law school, she repeated some of the same phrases she had used to describe her experiences very early in high school prior to her involvement with Rick, "I didn't understand what was going on." She reported that "law school was the opposite of my undergrad experience." For Loretta, the most difficult aspect of law school was their use of the Socratic method. This style of learning was difficult for her to follow and was contradictory to her usual way of studying and learning new information.

Loretta also described other aspects of law school that were challenging for her: "I had to take early morning classes and all my classes were chosen for me so I couldn't pick courses I knew I would like. Also, I hesitated to ask questions to avoid looking like an idiot." Loretta struggled considerably in law school, especially in her first year, where her grades were much lower than in high school or college. Her first-year grades included three classes in the C range, three in the B range, and one just passing. This was far less than she had done in her college grades and much below what she expected of herself. Despite this, she was able to complete her law school degree in the usual three years due to her exceptionally strong verbal comprehension abilities and her fierce determination to succeed.

After completing law school Loretta found a position in a law firm where she had very little contact with clients. Because of her very strong abilities in doing research she was hired to analyze and organize information for a very large team of attorneys who worked on complicated legal matters involving very large corporations. She was very good at this work, but she rarely engaged in any social contacts with other attorneys in her firm.

After her initial months working in this relatively isolated position, Jessica began to experience increasing frustration with her persisting ADHD impairments which were no longer attenuated by the intensive support of someone like Rick and no longer alleviated by her working in high interest projects collaborating with colleagues and mentors such as she had found in college. She became increasingly bored with her job. She struggled with sustaining attention and focus, modulating her processing speed and utilizing her short-term memory—problems that made it difficult for her to hold in mind multiple sentences, numbers, facts or words while reading and writing.

In her free time Loretta rekindled an earlier interest in doing art projects or making improvements in her home, often staying up very late engaged in these solitary activities and then struggling to get in to work for the required starting time in the morning. She was invited to join a small group of women in her firm who occasionally gathered together to attend plays or musical theatre. She sometimes joined in those events, but mostly she kept to herself. As she described her lack of social interaction, Loretta repeated several times, but unconvincingly, "I'm pretty content on my own."

She also continued to repeat:

> I feel like I'm failing in life and in my work. I'm not enjoying my work. I'm much slower to complete tasks and tend to put things off until the last possible minute. I feel steadily stressed and I'm eating too much, I've gained 50 pounds over the past year. I've read your book, *Smart but Stuck*, and I feel like I have a lot of the problems you described in those people with ADHD.

In the course of the initial consultation, it became clear that Loretta did, in fact, have ADHD. On the Brown Executive Function/Attention Scale she scored in the "very significant ADHD-related impairment" range. Clinical interview data also indicated that Loretta was clearly suffering from persistent depressive disorder, a type of depression that does not totally immobilize daily functioning, but significantly diminishes pleasure and enthusiasm even for activities previously enjoyable. I administered the Social Responsiveness Scale–2 and was not surprised to find that Loretta's responses yielded a score in the range that indicates "deficiencies in reciprocal social behavior that are clinically significant and lead to substantial interference with everyday social interactions. Such scores are typical for persons with autism spectrum disorders of moderate severity."

This summary assessment from the SRS-2 was accurate in recognizing that the characteristics Loretta claimed in her responses to the items of that scale typical of persons with an autism spectrum disorder. However, that scale could not recognize the importance of conflict within this woman over her wish to be closer to another person versus her felt need to pull back from emotional closeness. Loretta herself clearly expressed her dilemma in a statement quoted early in this chapter:

> I wanted to get married to him, but at the same time I didn't want to get married. I kept going back and forth. Sometimes I wanted the closeness and other times I wanted to pull away. He got frustrated with that and I just told him it would be better to end it.

This self-description by Loretta is somewhat similar to, yet quite different from, the statement by John Robison quoted in Chapter 1 of this book. In his autobiography he wrote:

> Many descriptions of autism and Asperger's describe people like me as "not wanting contact with others" or "preferring to play alone." ... I did not ever want to be alone ... I played by myself because I was a failure at playing with others. I was alone as a result of my own limitations, and being alone was one of the bitterest disappointments of my young life ... however robotic we Aspergians might seem, we do have deep feelings.
> (Robison, 2008, p. 211)

What Loretta's statement adds is that, like many other persons, she not only wanted to connect with someone, she also struggled with chronic and intense conflict between her wishes to get closer to a particular person by getting married vs. her wishes to avoid the discomfort or perceived risks in developing emotional closeness and commitments with that person. As she described her relationship with James it seemed very clear that Loretta felt a longing to get closer to James and eventually to marry him. She mentioned that she had sometimes thought about what it might be like to become James's wife and perhaps eventually to become a mother and raise a child with him. Yet she also said that she could not let herself think such thoughts very often or for very long.

Apparently her longings for such emotional closeness and commitment were accompanied by powerful fears about whether she could be comfortable with such intimacy over a long term and whether James would want to sustain such an intimate commitment to her. It was difficult to know how much of her worry was fueled by concerns about whether James might eventually lose interest in her and how much she feared she might be unable to sustain her wanting to be with him. Loretta dealt with that ambivalence by ending the relationship with James.

It is important to recognize the centrality of this conflict, this fundamental ambivalence about emotional closeness, that may be especially strong in persons who have tended to be loners during their childhood and adolescence. Lacking experience in the ups and downs of friendships during elementary and high school years when one usually gets some practice in surviving rebuffs and rejections, sometimes repairing them and sometimes grieving and moving on, those loners tend to feel more vulnerable in experimenting with emotional closeness as adults.

Loretta was quite clear in recognizing her intense ambivalence about wanting to get closer to James. One possible explanation for Loretta's breaking off her engagement with James might be that she took the initiative to end it so she could avoid the anticipated pain of having him reject her as he got to know her better.

As my initial consultation with Loretta was coming to a close, it had become clear that there were two major difficulties facing Loretta. One was her untreated ADHD that was continuing to interfere with her work and her social relationships. The other was her escalating depression, and her feelings of failure and hopelessness. These feelings of being a failure seemed to be fueled by Loretta's progressive losses of Rick, the supportive professors in her college, and then her decision to break off her relationship with James, the one she had once thought to be destined to be her life-partner. In the process of ending that engagement Loretta relieved herself of the immediate stress over getting more involved and possibly getting married to James, but she also intensified her feeling of being a failure at something she very much expected and wanted to do.

The intensifying depression which had escalated at the time of Loretta's 40th birthday reflects a pattern common among many persons with Asperger syndrome. Studies by Marriage et al. (2009) and others have shown that individuals whose Asperger syndrome or high functioning autism was not diagnosed until adulthood tended to have much higher incidence of depression, as high as 77%, than do those diagnosed with an autism spectrum diagnosis in early childhood or early adolescence.

In their study of adults diagnosed with Asperger syndrome only after reaching adulthood, Lehnhardt et al. (2012) reported that many "described feelings of strangeness and 'otherness' beginning by late adolescence that made them uncomfortable and insecure with respect to their ability to engage in meaningful intimate relationships." In another study of persons diagnosed with Asperger syndrome only after reaching adulthood, Jones et al. (2014) reported that, for many, the impetus for their seeking psychiatric assistance was a critical negative event such as loss of employment or the breakup of a significant relationship.

My recommendations for Loretta included medications for her ADHD and for her persistent depression. I offered to consult with her and her physician if they wanted consultation about her responses to these medications. I also advised Loretta that medications alone would not be likely to suffice for helping her alleviate her persistent depression. I suggested that she seek ongoing psychotherapy to assist her in sorting out underlying factors contributing to her persisting depression, particularly her strongly conflicting feelings about her ending the relationship with James. I offered the possibility of getting ongoing psychotherapy via Skype with me if she was unable to find a therapist in her area with whom she felt comfortable. We had no further contact with her after that day.

Reflections on Loretta and Beyond

Loretta's description of her struggles in high school suggests that in addition to ADHD she also had an undiagnosed language or learning disorder. She was clearly very bright, but her description of her high school experiences and her struggles in law school suggested that she suffered from some sort of language processing disorder.

Tannock and Brown (2009) have summarized research on the high frequency of overlap between ADHD and language and/or learning disorders. The range over various studies indicates that 25–40% of individuals with ADHD also meet diagnostic criteria for a specific learning disorder such as reading disorder, disorder of written expression or math disorder. Among those identified with a specific learning disorder about 15–40% also meet diagnostic criteria for ADHD.

Often those with these dual difficulties are recognized and provided intervention for one, but not for the other. In the case of Loretta, however, there had been no recognition of her having a specific language processing disorder prior to high school, but she reported considerable difficulty in processing much of the language of instruction in her classes without translation and support from Rick and she also reported similar problems in law school. However, it did seem that as she progressed through high school and college Loretta was considerably less impaired in her language use than she had been earlier.

Among those who are very bright, it is often difficult to disentangle ADHD and specific learning or language disorders. Also, Loretta's experience in high school may have caused her to exaggerate her difficulties in understanding what was being taught because that became the focus for her very intense and important relationship with Rick over the course of her high school years.

The most striking feature of Loretta's story is her intense ambivalence about James, the man with whom she had been engaged for four years. She very clearly identified her fundamental ambivalence about wanting to get closer to James to develop a lasting relationship with him and, at the same time, her strong discomfort about getting involved in a sustained intimate relationship with him, her wish to pull away. My brief time with her did not allow for much exploration of that conflict, but clearly that relationship was torn and eventually disrupted by intense fear in Loretta and then apparently persisting regret as well as relief.

It should be noted, however, that intense ambivalence about entering or staying in an intimate relationship is not limited to persons on the autism spectrum. Many who have none of the impairments of Asperger syndrome have intensely ambivalent feelings before engaging in an intimate partnership. And among people in the general population of the U.S. who do marry, about 50% end up getting divorced at least once.

Several research studies report that most adults with high-functioning autism spectrum disorder, including those diagnosed late in their life course, are either living alone or with their family of origin (usually their parents). Yet about 16–27% are either married or living with a partner and about 16% of those people have children (Hofvander et al., 2009; Joshi et al., 2013; Lehnhardt, 2012).

In providing treatment for people with Asperger syndrome, some therapists might feel pressure to encourage someone like Loretta to move forward in trying to develop a relationship such as she had with James. My consultation with her was not long enough to engage in such issues. However, in general, therapists in such situations are likely to be more helpful to such patients if they provide help in exploring both sides of the expressed ambivalence while avoiding any efforts, explicit or subtle, to tilt the table in either direction. Whatever the outcome, it is not the therapist who will live with the consequences.

As for living independently, despite her frustrations, Loretta was supporting herself and maintaining her own household independent of her family. Among adults whose autistic characteristics are not diagnosed until adolescence or adulthood, studies show that about 50% of those with such late diagnosis of autism spectrum are living in their own residence, some with varying levels of support from their family or government. More discussion of various factors in ultimate outcome of those with Asperger syndrome is provided in the Chapter 15 of this book.

13 Gary

I started coaching Little League just after I graduated from high school. Quickly I gained a reputation as a kind and very successful coach and a good motivator for young athletes. As a high school teacher I use those same skills to educate and motivate my students. Despite my continuing success as a coach and teacher, I have always been very private and isolated from most of those my own age. I got married and we had a child, but the marriage collapsed because of the lack of emotional connection between us.

Gary was 20 years old when he came to see me shortly after his stepfather had died of cancer. He had never known his biological father and had never developed a strong relationship with his stepfather, but the death of his stepfather left him living alone in their home with his mother who had a long history of severe mental illness. She was able to work competently as a registered nurse at a nursing home, but, except for going to work, she was very reclusive, maintaining contact only with Gary, her elderly parents, her one sister, and her now deceased husband. From time to time Gary's mother would mention to him her worry that other people could read her mind. Her psychotic symptoms were reasonably controlled so long as she consistently took her prescribed medication, but Gary was aware that his mother had twice required psychiatric hospitalization before he had been born and that she had many irrational fears about other people.

The reason for Gary's seeking treatment with me was not that he was overwhelmed with grief over the death of his stepfather. Rather, he reported that he had been increasingly anxious and depressed for several months prior to his stepfather's death. Gary was very concerned that his own mental health was deteriorating and that he might be suffering progressively from the mental illness that had impacted his mother at a comparable age.

At the time of that initial visit Gary was a sophomore enrolled in a local college while he lived at home. He appeared to be very bright and was quite articulate. He was studying to become a teacher and had been very successfully involved in volunteer coaching for youth baseball and basketball teams for a couple of years. He reported that he was very well liked and respected by the players he was coaching and by their parents. But he reported that over recent months he had begun to fear that he was gradually losing his mind.

DOI: 10.4324/9781003141976-18

I asked Gary many questions about his daily functioning and about what led him to believe that his mind was deteriorating. From his responses, it became clear that his mind was very much intact. There were no indications of any thought disorder. What I found were clear indications that Gary was harboring strong fears that he might eventually succumb to the same mental illness as his mother. This is an example of what has been called "struggle against identification," a term used to describe fears that some have that they will take on problematic aspects of personality characteristics or cognitive-behavioral problems of someone to whom they are related.

I told Gary that I found no reason to believe that he was becoming mentally ill, but I also mentioned that he seemed to be struggling with two problems. First, a lot of fears about himself that he had been trying to avoid for a long time, fears that were not surprising, given his family situation. Second, he also was reporting longstanding difficulties in completing many of his school assignments, despite doing very well on most tests and examinations.

When he came for his next session Gary handed me a typed single-spaced three-page paper in which he had summarized some autobiographical information to help me understand him. He wanted to read it aloud to me. Here are some excerpts:

> Up until fifth grade I had a fairly normal childhood, a normal circle of friends and a best friend I had a lot in common with, similar personalities, we hung out at each other's house almost every day in elementary school. I was playing little league baseball, was a good pitcher and got picked to play on the All-Star team of our league. In school I was seen as a really smart kid. Often other kids and our teacher would try, usually unsuccessfully, to stump me with brain-teasers. I had a pretty good personality and was well-liked.
>
> Starting in fifth grade I used to go to the school nurse a lot with stomach pain and nausea. In baseball I was getting extra coaching for my pitching. I pitched a solid summer, really enjoyed it, then fell apart with a series of panic attacks. I played my last baseball game in early September when I was 11 years old and then took off my uniform and never went back to playing baseball. My anxiety and panic attacks made it impossible.

What was striking to me about Gary's account of his Little League career was the utter absence of any parental support in situations where most kids come to each game with one or both parents to support and encourage them, as well as to console them when they are upset over having performed poorly or because their team had lost the game. Gary's notes elaborated on how he had become increasingly imprisoned in severe social anxiety:

> I spent more and more time alone and my grades immediately tanked after I quit baseball ... I made high honors throughout fifth grade, but never again through high school graduation ... but at that time the internet age was beginning and I found in it access to a wealth of information and a social

anonymity … I used it to begin making myself an expert in baseball, following specific teams and learning about all their players.

Despite his being socially avoidant after fifth grade, Gary had a period of about six months during eighth grade when he experimented with a different type of interaction with his classmates. He described that brief period as foreshadowing a style of interacting that he often utilized in later years. He developed a style of self-deprecating humor that brought him some months of popularity with his classmates:

> Everyone at age 12, 13, 14 is trying to build themselves up, hide their flaws and seem cooler or smarter or richer or better-looking than their peers. I took the opposite approach. I'd poke fun at my obvious flaws with great success, beat others to the punch by saying what they were thinking about me … and the popular kids sort of envied it, they didn't know what to make of it, but I became the humorist of the cool kids … I was just such a carefree, easygoing person to be around, they opened up to me, both genders, but especially the girls, because I was so non-threatening … I was nervous out of my mind, but I "performed" … but it was very short-lived.

Gary explained that when he and his classmates entered high school most of those "cool kids" were going to parties and getting drunk every weekend, he "fell right off the social map. Once you refuse to go out on enough Friday nights, people stop asking." His social anxiety intensified in the high school setting: "by the middle of ninth grade I had gone full circle, back to the nobody I had been for the first 2 years of middle school after I quit baseball." For his first two years of high school Gary immersed himself in his interest in sports journalism and writing on the internet:

> In high school I began to get into sports journalism. I was writing a lot and was published repeatedly on a number of fairly well-read baseball websites. I got a reputation among other students as someone who was really smart, but didn't do much schoolwork, yet was getting recognized at my school for writing smart articles about baseball that got published on the internet.

Yet he was not very fully engaged in his schoolwork:

> I started high school with several honors classes, but within a couple of semesters I got dropped from most of them because I almost never did much of the homework. During my junior year I said little and did little in most of my classes, but I would often be outspoken in English, my one remaining honors class. I would come into class not having read the assigned book, but I would outdebate students, some of whom are now at Ivy League Schools, who had read the whole book and taken detailed notes the night before.

I would listen to them make their prepared points early in the class, then from their comments I would figure out what the reading was about, the basic plot, and also I'd pay attention to the wording where I thought they were missing the meaning. Instantly my mind would develop rebuttals to the conclusions they were drawing, and then I'd find some quote in the pages near what they were quoting and use that other quote to rip them down. I got a C+ in that class because the teacher found my class participation so insightful that she overlooked the fact that I didn't do half the work. But I wasn't improving academically.

After hearing Gary's description of his difficulties in middle school and high school, I asked him how he was doing now that he was in college. He reported that he found a lot of the work not very challenging, but was getting passing grades, though he often struggled to keep up with his assignments, except in classes he found especially interesting either because of the content or because the professor was a really interesting lecturer. These comments led me to ask Gary questions about his difficulties in completing his work and then to administer the Brown Executive Function/Attention Scale. Results from that scale and from clinical interviews indicated that, in addition to his depression and social anxiety, Gary also fully met diagnostic criteria for ADHD. To alleviate his ADHD impairments we began a trial of Vyvanse with an Adderall booster in mid-afternoon. That combination was quite helpful in helping Gary to manage his college studies more adequately.

Shortly after starting the stimulants for ADHD we arranged for Gary to begin a trial of Wellbutrin-XL which helped to alleviate somewhat his chronic depression and anxiety. After adjustments of the dosing, Gary found that he was much better able to apply himself to his studies and began to feel less anxious and depressed. Another factor which helped to reduce Gary's worry about losing his cognitive strengths was my administering to him the WAIS-IV IQ test. He had never had an IQ test and wanted to see how he would measure up. Gary was quite pleased when he found that he had scored in the very superior range at the 99th percentile for his age. At this point we agreed that Gary would begin a course of ongoing psychotherapy with me.

Meanwhile Gary was becoming increasingly involved in coaching youth sports, both baseball and basketball. He moved from being a volunteer coach for youth leagues to being a paid coach for a middle school team and a paid assistant coach for a local high school team. He really enjoyed his coaching and quickly became quite respected and well-liked by players, their parents and other coaches. He completed his student teaching requirement where he quickly gained a reputation for being an exceptionally good teacher. Shortly after graduating from college he got a job as a high school math teacher for the following school year.

Meanwhile, for the summer, Gary got a job as a counselor at a high-end sleepover camp where he quickly became a very popular cabin counselor and athletic instructor. However, though he was very involved in interactions with the campers, he tended to avoid much social interaction with the other counselors, most of whom were his age. He described them as follows:

> an extremely impressive group of young adults who did a good job with the kids, but also spent a lot of time together socializing in a relaxed way that I just didn't fit into. Most evenings after the campers were asleep, I read for several hours alone in my cabin rather than joining other counselors in their lounge. On my weekly day off, I drove to a small town near the camp and spent most of the day hiking alone in the nearby hills and then reading in the local library. I felt comfortable only when I was interacting with the campers and maintaining my usual solitary lifestyle.

Gary completed the summer camp job and then began his first year of being a full-time teacher while continuing his coaching of youth basketball and baseball where he was gaining increasing success while also developing a reputation as a very well-organized and appealing teacher. I met with him occasionally during his two years of teaching in that school. In one of those conversations he read me a description of his long-standing enjoyment of late-night talk shows:

> Conan O'Brien and other late-night talk show hosts fascinate me. In real life they were anonymous by choice, relentlessly private people who never graced the red carpet or dated Hollywood starlets. Letterman's personal life was a complete mystery. O'Brien was a Harvard-educated bookworm who went to great pains to disguise his appearance when he went out in public ... Despite their disdain for the spotlight, they were remarkably gifted performers. On a nightly basis they hosted wildly popular television shows named after them that attracted millions of viewers ... O'Brien used a devastating gift for self-deprecation to always turn one of his guests' stories into a connection with his own clumsiness and inadequacy. It was always about him, but he was insulting himself, and we laughed with him and forgave his self-absorption.
>
> I viewed myself as someone with the same oddball, blatantly contradictory combination of social introversion and love of self and stage. I felt I could talk about myself in a way that was clever and charismatic enough that you'd want to listen, but I only wanted to do it on my own terms. It had to be my show.

After hearing this I asked Gary if he still felt that same contradiction in himself between a need to remain very private and solitary while also being outgoing in the way he presented himself to others. He readily agreed and explained that in his interactions with his students and with the young athletes he coached, he was quite lively, outgoing, and entertaining, while he remained private and solitary in his personal life, spending virtually all the time he was away from his jobs by himself. He lived alone and did not socialize at all with other teachers, other coaches, the parents of the players on teams he coached or with his neighbors. He said he simply did not feel comfortable spending unstructured time with other adults. When in the role of teacher or coach for younger people he was able to "do it on his own terms" safely within in a clearly defined role and status. Outside that structure, his Asperger traits were much more apparent as they were when he was a camp counselor after the campers went to sleep.

After his second year of teaching Gary relocated to another state where he was to begin a new teaching position with a significantly better salary. He was not able to return regularly to meet with me, though we had occasional conversations by phone during which he reported considerable success in his teaching although he also mentioned that he had not yet developed any friendships with neighbors or other teachers in his school.

Shortly after that school year concluded I was contacted by Gary who had gotten himself admitted to the psychiatric unit of a hospital in the state where he had been working. He explained that he had become acutely depressed after that school year ended because a young woman for whom he had developed an intense platonic attachment had rejected his efforts to continue their friendship. She explained this by telling him that she was a lesbian and was moving away to live with another woman with whom she had developed a committed relationship.

This loss of his first-ever effort to develop a relationship with a woman plummeted Gary into an acute depressive reaction with frightening suicidal thoughts. He went to a nearby hospital where he was admitted to the psychiatric ward where he stayed for several weeks.

Gary came to see me after he was discharged from that hospital. With him was a woman his own age who had been a patient in that psychiatric unit during his stay. Her name was Linda. Gary reported that the two of them had discovered that they both suffered from some similar problems and had some impressive strengths. They had decided to try sharing Gary's apartment as an experiment in living together for a while.

One month later Gary returned for a follow-up during which he reported that his relationship with Linda had developed rapidly:

> Our relationship has now become sexual and we are both enjoying that. It's my first experience, but not hers. We got engaged last week and we're planning to get married in two months. Linda has been working at a clothing store, but that will be just short term because I just finalized arrangements for a new teaching job I had applied for at a really nice independent school with an excellent reputation. It's halfway across the country, so we'll have to move. But it's a great opportunity. Linda and I are going to move there in a couple of weeks so we can be settled before the fall term starts.

Eight weeks later Gary phoned to report that he and Linda were getting settled in their new home and he was about to begin his new teaching job. He enthusiastically reported that they had gotten married as planned and had found a nice house to rent. He also reported that Linda had already started a new job working as a nanny for a family with several kids and she liked it.

Several months later Gary called to report that things had been going well in his job and in their marriage. He was pleased that Linda had made a collage for him in celebration of his birthday. My next communication from Gary was about four months later. He called to report that Linda had become pregnant. He also mentioned that he had been working very long hours with his teaching and coaching, often coming home quite tired. We agreed that he would ask his physician to add a booster dose of Adderall to provide better coverage for late afternoon and early evening. I also encouraged Gary to try to spend some extra time with his wife as she was coping with the pressures of the pregnancy. Seven months later I received an email from Gary announcing the birth of their son. I sent congratulations to both proud parents.

We had no further communication until almost a year later when Gary emailed me saying that he and his wife had separated and he wanted to talk. We had a phone consultation in which Gary explained that both Linda and he had both been depressed and "just not clicking" during recent months. Both enjoyed their son, but they had found that caring for an infant is a lot of work. Gary said that Linda had been complaining that he had been helping some with care of the baby, but she felt that Gary was not showing enough attention to her.

Now Linda had taken the baby and had flown home to spend some time with her mother. She had also contacted a lawyer and had not bought a return ticket. Gary said that he had been talking with Linda by phone every night over the week since she left, trying to reassure her that he loved her and wanted her to return home so they could improve their relationship and continue to raise their son together. His impression from those conversations was that Linda had been getting a lot of encouragement from her mother to give up on the marriage. In those calls he had emphasized that he wanted to be with Linda and wanted to share with her in raising their son.

As we talked Gary decided that he would take some time off from work and immediately fly to meet face-to-face with Linda for conversation and to see their son where she was staying at her mother's home. He called me two days later reporting that he had talked with Linda and found that she was determined to end the marriage as soon as possible, but she was willing to return home to live separately from Gary while arrangements for divorce were made.

Gary returned home and soon engaged an attorney who advised him that Linda could not legally keep their son out of state to live separately without Gary's agreement or a court ruling establishing a divorce. His attorney also advised Gary to start the process of filing for divorce while also trying to get Linda to return home immediately and talk with him further to see if any reconciliation could be worked out. Gary was devastated and reported intense depressive symptoms with severe sleep disruption. I encouraged him to consult with a local psychiatrist to get appropriate changes in his medication. Linda returned a few days later and arranged for her own attorney as well as separate living arrangements. The two attorneys worked out a mutually agreeable temporary agreement for shared custody of their son while arrangements for divorce were completed.

The divorce of Gary and Linda was finalized ten months later, despite several efforts by Gary to arrange for some joint therapy sessions to see if their problems could be resolved. Gary reported that it had soon become evident that Linda had an intimate relationship with another man. Gary continued to spend as much time with their son as was allowed by the custody agreement. Eventually, after another year, he developed a relationship with another woman while continuing to be intensively involved with his son on an alternating week custody schedule.

Reflections on Gary and Beyond

Gary's "struggle against identification" with his mother's debilitating depressions and psychotic thinking was just one of the painful consequences of his growing up without ever knowing his father and with a mother who was herself quite reclusive and fearful of other people. She loved him and provided some financial support, but she was extremely limited in her ability to provide him with the encouragement and emotional support he desperately needed. It is quite impressive that Gary did so well without anyone to support him from the sidelines as he played Little League games or to show continuing interest in how well he was or was not doing in his schoolwork. The fact that his ADHD was not recognized until he was struggling in college and sought help for his anxiety and depression further complicated his already difficult social and academic development.

Gary persevered and successfully completed college and became a successful, well-liked teacher, as well as a skilled coach for youth sports. His ADHD impairments and depression were alleviated considerably by appropriate medication that he started in college and continued thereafter. His Asperger characteristics did not significantly impair his work as a teacher or his coaching youth sports. He was very successful in both of those roles, though his social-emotional impairments did cause him considerable difficulty in his efforts to develop closer personal relationships.

Gary had maintained some contact with two male friends from high school with whom he occasionally communicated by email or text, but his friendship with the young lesbian woman whom he had met while working at the camp was his first effort to develop a close friendship with a woman. It began with a series of conversations about various matters at the camp and gradually led to a series of late-night conversations about current political events in which both were interested. As Gary explained the relationship to me, he had no interest in trying to develop any sexual involvement with the woman; he spoke of himself at that time as "asexual," having no sexual interests in anyone.

Yet, despite the platonic nature of that relationship, Gary developed an intense intellectualized infatuation with the woman even though she had clearly told him of her ongoing relationship with her partner. He tended to ignore this while trying to intensify their friendly interaction; he expressed resentment about any efforts by the woman's partner to spend more time with her rather than with him. Meanwhile, he told two lies about himself to both the woman and her lover. He claimed that he had an ongoing relationship with a girlfriend; he also told them that he was enrolled in a program to study for a doctoral degree.

Eventually Gary felt need to confess the two lies to the two women. This led to intense resentment from both of them, especially the lover of the woman he felt closer to. That led to the rupture of his relationship with both those women shortly before they moved to another state. It was the loss of that relationship that precipitated the depression which led Gary to seek psychiatric hospitalization.

Gary's difficulties in understanding and sustaining emotional relationships also became clear in his rapidly intensifying involvement with Linda, the woman he met while both were patients in the psychiatric hospital. Within the hospital program they had together participated in twice daily group sessions structured to encourage participants to be open in sharing their feelings and impressions with one another. Gary reported that he energetically participated in those group sessions and that Linda had quickly become attracted to him in that setting. It was she who had proposed to him that they try living together immediately after they were discharged.

When Gary described to me his experiences as patient in that psychiatric hospital, I recalled how he had spoken about his strong interest in late-night show hosts who were quite private in their personal lives though talking freely about themselves during their performance on their shows. His statement mentioned earlier in this chapter described his conflicting feelings about self-disclosure and his need to control his relationships on his own terms:

> I viewed myself as someone with the same oddball, blatantly contra-dictory combination of social introversion and love of self and stage. I felt I could talk about myself in a way that was clever and charismatic enough that you'd want to listen, but I only wanted to do it on my own terms. It had to be my show.

With these words he described his persisting social anxiety in part of eighth grade juxtaposed with his strong wish to present himself to others openly as interesting and articulate. He also emphasized in those words his need to "do it on my own terms" in a way that he could control and protect himself. From Gary's description, it sounded as though the initial enthusiasm he and Linda felt about their living together immediately after leaving the hospital, their move together out of state, their marriage, and their getting their own home lasted for some months, gradually diminished. Gary had gradually become more solitary, less empathetic, and more distant from his wife.

Even before Linda became pregnant, Gary was complaining that he had been working long hours and coming home very tired after his teaching and coaching. We talked about his feeling that he did not have much time or energy to give to his wife. When their baby came, Gary reported that Linda acknowledged that he was helping with childcare, but he also noted that she had been complaining that she felt she was not getting enough time, attention, or support from Gary. He was not able to read the escalating frustration she was experiencing, and he was shocked when she suddenly left with their baby to visit her mother, who lived almost two thousand miles away, and had not purchased a return ticket. When it became clear to him that his efforts to persuade Linda to work with him to improve their marriage were not working, he became acutely depressed just as he had when he realized that his earlier relationship with the lesbian woman was over. He had not been able to see either of those losses coming.

Some people with Asperger syndrome avoid forming close personal relationships; some try to make such relationships work, and enjoy some temporary success, but have great difficulty in sustaining the close relationship; and some eventually get such relationships to work. When it became clear that divorce was unavoidable, Gary continued to sustain his close relationship with his son and soon sought a new relationship with another woman.

Part V

Updates on ADHD, Asperger Syndrome and Overlap

14 ADHD

Problems in the Brain's Self-Management System

When thinking of ADHD, many imagine a mischievous little boy who is constantly restless and rarely listens to what people say to him. That stereotype of ADHD as simply a behavior problem of young children has been replaced with science-based understanding of ADHD as a complex problem in the unfolding development of the brain's self-management system—its executive functions. This chapter describes that new understanding.

This new understanding recognizes ADHD as not a simple problem of hyperactive behavior or inability to listen when someone is speaking. This new view could be stated in a simple equation: **ADHD = developmental impairment of executive functions**, the complex set of brain functions that serve as each person's self-management system. Beginnings of these executive functions emerge in preschool years and develop very gradually from early school years through to late adolescence and early adulthood. Executive functions are not fully developed in most persons until late teens or early twenties.

Everyone understands that there are some tasks that a 9-year-old child can do which simply cannot be managed by a three-year old. Likewise, most 12-year-olds are able to manage tasks they could not have managed when they were 8 years old. The reason that most states will not allow anyone under the age of 16 or 18 years to drive a motor vehicle is not that their legs are too short to reach the pedals. It is because in their earlier years they would not yet have the abilities needed to focus and responsibly manage the rapidly changing complexities of safely driving a motor vehicle in traffic.

When we talk about "focus" in ADHD, we are not referring to "focus" as in "focus the camera." It is more like what is meant when we say "focus on your driving." When driving, one does not simply stare at the bumper of the car ahead. One watches that car, but also is checking the rear-view mirror and side view mirror and monitoring surrounding traffic. The driver also is alert to a truck backing out of a driveway and to a few pedestrians running across the street to catch a bus. Meanwhile, that driver may be shifting over to the left lane to prepare for making a turn and, noticing that the stoplight is turning

DOI: 10.4324/9781003141976-20

from green to red, he will be taking his foot off the accelerator and moving it to the brake. At the same time the driver may be thinking about what he needs to buy when he arrives at the grocery store. Focusing on one's driving involves noticing many quickly changing events and situations, ignoring some, keeping some in mind and rechecking others. It involves performing multiple tasks in order safely to drive the car to get to a destination.

ADHD involves those functions of the brain that allow one to manage a wide variety of frequently shifting tasks of daily life. When a person is diagnosed with ADHD, it means that the child, adolescent or adult has not yet developed the ability to manage themselves adequately to do tasks of daily life which would usually be expected for most others of their particular age.

ADHD affects about 9% to 11% of children and at least 4% or 5% of adults in the U.S. Sometimes ADHD appears in early childhood, but often it does not become apparent until the individual reaches the challenges of middle school, high school, or beyond. Research has shown that while some children outgrow their ADHD impairments, for most, these difficulties persist into late adolescence and continue into adulthood.

Figure 14.1 summarizes a model that identifies six clusters of executive functions often impaired in ADHD. Each cluster represents a grouping of brain management functions, but these functions are not actually separate. They tend to work together in different combinations to manage various tasks a person is faced with, starting with very simple tasks like getting dressed or speaking a sentence to much more complex tasks like crossing a busy street, carrying on a conversation, preparing a meal, or driving a car.

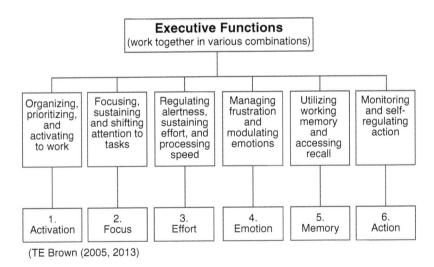

Figure 14.1 Executive Functions Impaired in ADHD

Four Basic Facts about this Model of ADHD Impairments

(A) **All the problems included here as impairments of executive functions are problems everyone experiences sometimes.** Those who warrant a diagnosis of ADHD are individuals who are more often and more severely impaired in these executive functions relative to others of similar age. ADHD is not an all-or-nothing classification like pregnancy. It is more like depression in that everyone feels sad and unhappy sometimes, but we do not diagnose anyone as being clinically depressed simply because they feel sad or unhappy for a couple of days. It is only when those symptoms are significantly impairing for a person on a more ongoing basis that we say: "This is a depression which needs to be treated." In the same way we do not say that a person has ADHD if they have these executive function difficulties only occasionally and are not significantly impaired much of the time compared with others of comparable age.

(B) **Executive functions operate very quickly and usually without much conscious thought.** Except for novel situations which require more thoughtful planning and movements, executive functions usually operate so automatically that one does not need consciously to think about each action. They are mostly performed unconsciously, not in the old psychoanalytic sense of repression, but in the more modern sense of automaticity.

(C) **Executive functions impaired in ADHD are a heritable syndrome.** Despite the diversity of the six clusters included in the model above, they tend usually to appear together as a syndrome. Executive function impairments represented in this model are highly heritable. Among persons diagnosed with ADHD about one in four has a parent with ADHD. The remaining three usually have at least one other close blood relative with ADHD: a sibling, grandparent, aunt, or uncle. The ADHD syndrome runs in families.

(D) **Executive function impairments of ADHD are "situationally variable."** All persons with ADHD tend to have a few tasks or activities for which they do not experience these impairments of executive function. Usually these exceptional situations involve activities the person finds very interesting or where they fear that something they consider quite unpleasant will happen very soon if they do not take care of this specific situation promptly here and now. More about situational variability appears later in this chapter as "The central mystery of ADHD."

Examples of Executive Function Impairments

One of the best ways to learn about executive functions impaired in ADHD is to listen to examples provided by persons with ADHD when they describe their difficulties in exercising these functions. In the following pages of this chapter each of the six clusters is briefly described. After each summary are examples from some adults, teenagers or children who have described their difficulties with that group of self-management functions.

Cluster 1
Activation: Getting Organized, Prioritizing, and Getting Started

The Activation cluster addresses difficulties individuals may have organizing tasks and materials, estimating time, prioritizing tasks, and getting started on work-like tasks (i.e., activities they have not usually chosen for pleasure). People with ADHD often have chronic difficulty with excessive procrastination. Often they will put off getting started on a task—even a task they recognize as important to them—until the very last minute. It is as though they cannot get themselves started until they perceive the task as an acute emergency or as something where delay is likely to result in some kind of punishment. Functions in this cluster involve problems with setting priorities and getting started, following instructions, keeping track of assigned tasks.

Difficulty Getting Started

An attorney with ADHD described his difficulty with prioritizing and getting started this way:

> All my life I've had trouble getting started on my work when I have to work by myself. I don't have any trouble when I'm talking with clients or working with other lawyers or working with the secretaries. But when I'm in my office and I've got paperwork to do, I just can't get myself started. A couple of times a week I set aside several hours for paperwork that I want to get done. I need to get it done because I don't get paid until it's done. I block out several hours to do it and I'm in my office with all the materials I need in front of me.
>
> But I just can't get myself to start it. Usually I end up turning on my computer and sitting in the office doing email, checking some news sites, and playing video games. I have to shut it off every time the secretary comes in so she doesn't see what I'm doing. The end of the day comes and my work isn't even started.
>
> I go home and have a bite to eat and watch some TV. Then about 10 p.m. I suddenly remember: "Oh, my God. I've got that report to do! I have to get it in by 8 a.m. tomorrow or I'm going to be in very serious trouble at work." At that point I don't have any problem getting started. I get on my home computer and work very efficiently from 10 p.m. to 2 a.m. and produce an excellent report. But it's a hell of way to have to live.

Like this attorney, many individuals with ADHD syndrome chronically delay in starting tasks until they are face-to-face with the immediate pressure of a significant deadline. They know the task needs to be done, but they ignore it until the last possible moment.

Difficulty Prioritizing and Organizing

Another example of difficulty in getting organized, prioritizing, and getting started is described by this homemaker who sought treatment for ADHD:

My husband said I couldn't organize a two-car funeral. It made me mad, but I guess he's right. When I have a bunch of things to do, they all seem equally important. Like when I'm cleaning the house. I try to straighten up the living room a little and I pick up yesterday's newspaper and then I start reading it. Then I go upstairs to get the vacuum cleaner and when I'm up there I see an envelope of photos I got developed last week. I sit down to put them in the album and then I get involved in looking at the other pictures in the album. It happens even with paying the bills. Often I just dump all the day's mail in a big basket and don't even sort it out.

Last month our mortgage bank and our electric company both phoned us because I hadn't paid them. We had the money, but for two months in a row I had left our mortgage statement and our electric bill in a pile of junk mail. I just don't seem to be able to say to myself, "OK, I've got all these things to take care of, this should be first and then this and then this." I'm not good at figuring out how to use whatever time or energy I have to take care of what I've got to do.

This description highlights several components in what might otherwise be assumed to be a single function. She describes a problem in scanning a range of tasks and discriminating among them; in assigning different weights of priority to various tasks confronting her. It's difficult for her to decide her priorities and then get started on them.

Cluster 2
Focus: Focusing, Sustaining, and Shifting Attention for Tasks

The Focus cluster addresses problems individuals may have in sustaining attention and focus for work-like tasks or in shifting attention when needed from one activity to another. For people with ADHD, it is often difficult to focus on a specific task and sustain their attention on that task. At times, they may be easily distracted by things going on around them or by thoughts in their own mind. At other times, they may find themselves stuck on one thing, unable to shift to another task even when directed to do so.

Sustaining Focus When Listening

One of the most common complaints of persons with ADHD is that they cannot focus their attention on a task and keep focusing as long as necessary. One high school student compared his problem to the difficulty of losing the radio signal when driving too far away from the radio station:

In my classes I always get part of what's being talked about. But no matter how hard I try, I keep losing track of what's happening. Like in Geometry I'll be listening while the teacher explains how to do this problem, and then I just drift off for a little bit. I come back and try to figure out where he is on this thing now, and then pretty soon I lose it again. And then I'll get another piece of it, but usually I don't know how he got to that because I had drifted off. Same thing happens in English and in History and in everything else. I just can't keep my mind on what's happening in class for more than a few minutes. I'm always drifting in and out.

It's sort of like what happens when you're listening to your car radio and you drive too far away from the station you're listening to. You know how the voice or the music starts going in and out on you? That's the way it is for me when I'm trying to listen to somebody talk. Most of the time I just can't keep myself tuned to what I'm trying to do.

Everyone experiences from time to time this difficulty in selecting and sustaining their focus. But those with ADHD report that they struggle much more than most of us throughout the day.

Difficulty in Filtering Distractions

Another facet of the problem of not being able to focus on an intended task is excessive distractibility. Even when they have focused on a task, whether reading, listening, or trying to do some other work, persons with ADHD often feel themselves drawn away by distractions. They cannot ignore the myriad thoughts, background noises, and perceptions in the surrounding environment.

I don't miss much of anything, except what I'm supposed to be paying attention to. When I'm working in my cubicle, I'm always listening in on what everybody else is doing. I just can't help myself. If one of the secretaries is talking on the phone two cubicles over, I'm listening in and trying to figure out what they're talking about. Meanwhile, I'm checking out what's going on across the hall at the coffee machine and who just went into the bathroom. It's not easy when I'm trying to follow a couple of different phone conversations at the same time.

Then too, I'm often "out to lunch" at meetings. If we're all sitting in the conference room reviewing some project, I'll be looking out the window watching some squirrel climb a tree or checking out the clouds going by or the guy mowing the lawn. Or I just drift off thinking of "whatever" and then I catch myself and realize that I've spaced out and have totally lost track of the group's conversation.

The scariest times with this are when I'm driving along the expressway and suddenly catch myself looking too long at a billboard while I'm coming up way too fast on a car that is slowing down in front of me because of a traffic jam that I hadn't seen coming. More than a few times I've had to hit my brakes fast and hard to prevent a collision. This "getting distracted" can get pretty dangerous.

Cluster 3
Effort: Regulating Alertness, Sustaining Effort, and Adjusting Processing Speed

The Effort cluster includes problems individuals may have in staying alert as well as settling into sleep and sustaining sufficient effort for work-related tasks. It also addresses difficulties with processing information, completing tasks, and maintaining performance efficiency. Many with ADHD can perform short-term projects well but have much more difficulty with sustained effort over longer periods of time. It may take them longer than others to process and react to what they see or hear, and they may find it difficult to complete tasks on time, especially when they need to do a writing task.

Many also experience chronic difficulty regulating their sleep and alertness. They often stay up too late simply because they can't stop themselves from thinking about things. Once asleep, however, they often sleep very soundly and have trouble getting up in the morning. At other times, they may become drowsy when not physically active or cognitively engaged, even when they have had sufficient rest. Items in this cluster involve difficulties staying interested in routine tasks long enough to finish them, giving up when things get difficult, requiring extra time to complete routine tasks, and having trouble sleeping at night or staying alert during the day.

Difficulty in Getting to Sleep and in Awakening

A man employed as an accountant described a different type of problem with sleep and with awakening:

> My mother tells me that from my first few months she always had a hard time getting me to settle down for sleep. I was never much of a nap-taker and always a night owl. She always said I didn't want to close my eyes because I was afraid I would miss out on some interesting action.
>
> I don't know what the reason is, but I do know that even today I still have a lot of trouble getting myself to fall asleep. I can be dead tired with my eyes blurry. Almost ready to collapse, I lie down on my bed but I just can't get my head to shut off so I can get to sleep. It just keeps going over whatever I've been thinking about. Usually I have to listen to music or watch TV so I can block that other stuff out and get to sleep.
>
> Once I get to sleep, I usually sleep like a dead person. They could drop a bomb in my bedroom and I wouldn't even notice. That was a big problem when I was in high school. I was always missing my bus and late for school. It took my parents about ten tries to get me up every day. They would make noise and pull the covers off of me and I'd just mumble or swear at them and roll over and go back to sleep. This is even when I had especially asked them to get me up on time so I wouldn't lose credit for my early classes.

It was even worse when I got to college because I couldn't wake up from any alarm clock and my roommates never wanted to take on the job of getting me out of bed. The only thing that worked was when I lived in the fraternity house and could make the pledges do it. Later, when I got married, my wife took it over.

Difficulty Sustaining Effort

A woman employed as a supervisor in a marketing firm complained of a different type of problem in working steadily for some tasks, though she had no difficulty in completing other tasks very efficiently:

> If I'm doing something that I can get done quickly in one chunk, I'm usually OK. I love it when people in the office call me to troubleshoot some problem in dealing with a client or even to help them fix some glitch in their computer. If I could do that kind of quick fix stuff all the time I would be a great worker.
>
> It's the long-term projects I have trouble with, the kind of thing where you can't get it done in one chunk in a few minutes or even in a few hours or a whole day—those projects where you have to keep chipping away at it because it just can't be done even in one day. I fade out fast on those things. I start out saying to myself, "OK, I'm really going to apply myself to this job and keep working steadily on it, one chunk a day until it's finished." But pretty soon I'm getting bored and losing interest.
>
> Usually I end up just saying to myself, "Hurry up, slap-dash. Let's just get this damn thing done without worrying about how good it is." Or sometimes I don't even get that far. I just put it off until it becomes more of an emergency. My mind is much more of a sprinter. It's never been much as a long-distance runner.

Difficulty Regulating Processing Speed

A girl in her senior year of high school reported difficulty in taking notes for her classes and in completing essay tests or writing assignments within a reasonable time:

> It takes me so long to get things written down. When I am taking notes on what the teacher is saying, I'm always trying to write down something from sentence two while everybody else in class is taking notes on sentence nine. I just can't keep up and write things down as fast as others in the class. Even if I'm just copying sentences off the whiteboard, it always takes me longer to get it copied than it does everybody else.
>
> And it's not just when I'm taking notes. When I am writing an essay or sentences to answer on a test, I never can get it out fast enough, regardless of how hard I try. My mind is fast in thinking about things and in

getting ideas, but I'm so slow in getting things written down. I feel like I'm a really fast computer with a really slow modem. It takes half of forever to upload or download the information I need.

Cluster 4
Emotion: Managing Frustration and Modulating Emotions

The Emotion cluster includes difficulties persons may have with regulating emotional reactions that may otherwise take over too much of what they are thinking or doing. Although the *DSM-5* does not recognize any symptoms related to emotion management as an aspect of ADHD, many with the syndrome describe chronic difficulties managing frustration, anger, fear, disappointment, worry, desire, and other emotions. They find it very difficult to put their emotions into perspective and get on with what they need to do.

Many speak as though these emotions, when experienced, take over their thinking the way a computer virus might infect a computer and make it impossible for them to attend adequately to anything else. Items in this cluster involve difficulties with excessive irritability, hypersensitivity to criticism, overwhelming worry, obsessively wanting something, immobilizing discouragement or other emotional dysregulation.

Difficulty Modulating Irritability

A middle-aged salesman described his disproportionate reactions to annoyance this way:

> I went to the diner for a late lunch. It was mid-afternoon and the place was fairly quiet. Most everybody else had already eaten. I was eating my sandwich and was in a pretty good mood. Then this guy sitting behind me got his sandwich and he was chewing too loud. "Chomp, chomp, chomp" with every bite. The sound of his noisy chewing quickly got on my nerves. It was driving me nuts.
>
> It was like I had a computer virus in my head and it was taking up all the space. That's all I could think about—the obnoxious sound of his chomping on his sandwich. Suddenly I realized my fists were clenched and I was seriously thinking about getting up and smacking this guy in the mouth! I didn't do it because I didn't want to get arrested. But if I had been at home, I would have been yelling at somebody.
>
> After a few minutes, it was all over. He was still making the same noises, but then it didn't bother me anymore. I just went on with my lunch and started thinking about something else. That sort of thing happens to me a lot though. Some frustration that most people would consider a zero, one, or two on a ten-point scale of frustration can hit me as though it were a seven, eight, or nine.

Excessive Sensitivity

Irritability and anger are not the only emotions problematic for those with ADHD. Many with ADHD have equal or greater difficulty modulating other emotions such as hurt, sadness, desire, worry or discouragement. A salesman in a large corporation told the following story about his problem with a different kind of emotional response:

> Last week in the office I was walking down the hall when I saw this friend who works in another department. He was reading some papers while he was walking. I said a friendly "Hi" and thought he would stop and visit for a couple of minutes because I hadn't seen him for a long time. But he just barely looked up and mumbled a quick "Hi" back to me and kept right on walking.
>
> Most people would blow that off right away, figuring he was just in a hurry to get some meeting or preoccupied with whatever he was reading. Not me. I got to thinking about it over and over. I kept wondering, "Why wasn't he more friendly? Have I done something to piss him off? Did I do something that annoyed somebody else in his department and now they're all mad at me?"
>
> This happened at lunch time, but all afternoon these thoughts kept going around in my head. It was like that a computer virus thing that gobbled up all the space in my head. I didn't get anything done for the rest of that day.

Excessive Urgency

A young father diagnosed with ADHD spoke about how he often gets too intense about something he wants to get or wants to do:

> I've never been a very patient person. When I get an idea in my head about something I want to do, or something I want to get, or something I want to buy, that wish takes on such intense urgency that I feel I've got to have this NOW! It almost doesn't matter how expensive it is, or how inconvenient it might be for me or somebody else, or whether I'll be using time or money today for this when I know I need that time or money tomorrow for something else that is more important. I feel this relentless drive to do everything I can to get whatever it is I want and to get it now, overcoming whatever obstacles might be put in my way.
>
> And then if I am able to get it, after a few minutes it usually isn't all that satisfying. I just had to have it, and then I've got it, and then I'm off to my next thing. I've always been that way, but I didn't realize it until I got mad at my ten-year-old son for pulling the same kind of stuff. After I finished yelling at him for it, my wife said to me, "Can't you see that he's only doing the same things you do yourself?" She was right.

There is no particular emotion that is problematic for all persons with ADHD syndrome, but most diagnosed with ADHD report one or several different emotions that they have significant difficulty managing.

Cluster 5
Memory: Utilizing Working Memory and Accessing Recall

The Memory cluster includes problems individuals may have with excessive forgetfulness in daily routines or in recall of recently acquired information. Very often people with ADHD will report that they have adequate or exceptional memory for things that happened long ago but great difficulty in remembering where they just put something, what they have just read, what someone has just said to them, or what they were about to say. They may describe having difficulty holding one or several things in mind while also attending to other tasks. In addition, many often complain that they cannot readily retrieve information they have recently studied or recently learned. Items in this cluster involve difficulties in remembering instructions, following through with planned activities, keeping track of belongings, and recalling information they have read minutes earlier or information recently studied.

Impaired Short-Term Memory

This homemaker compared her difficulties in working memory with having a multi-line telephone without a hold button.

> I'm really good at remembering things from a long time ago. I can tell you the whole story line from movies I saw just once years ago and haven't seen since. But even though I'm the best in my family for remembering things from way back, I'm the worst at remembering what happened just a few minutes ago. If I look up a phone number, I can never remember it long enough to dial it. I always have to write it down or I'll mix up the numbers.
>
> I'll go into a room to get something and then I'm standing there scratching my head wondering what I came in there for. Or I'll go to the store to get five things I need to fix dinner. If I don't write them down, I'll be able to pick up only two of them; I can't remember the other three to save my life.
>
> It's like my mind is a multi-line phone where the hold button doesn't work. If I am trying to remember one thing and then I set it aside even for just a minute to think about or do something else, I totally lose what I was trying to hold onto.

Difficulty in Recalling Learned Information

Students with ADHD syndrome often complain that they study diligently to prepare for an examination and can recall the material quite well when quizzed the night before the test, but then find that on the next day at the time of the test they are unable to recall a significant portion of material they readily knew the day before:

> It's so frustrating when I study hard for tests and then can't remember what I learned. I'll study hard and learn everything we're supposed to know. My friends quiz me and I've got it all down. Then, the next day I go in to take the test, figuring that I'm going to get a good grade. And then when I'm actually taking the test, a big chunk of what I knew so well the night before just evaporates.
>
> It's like I have a file in my computer and can't remember the file name to open it up. I know the stuff is in there, but I just can't get to it, so I can't put it down on the test. Then a few hours after the test, something will jog my memory and it's all back again. It's not that I didn't have it in there. It was in my mind, I just couldn't retrieve it when needed.

Need for Repeated Re-reading

Often students with ADHD report that it takes them excessively long to complete written examinations because they are not able to keep in mind what they have just read. One high school junior reported her experience of running out of time while taking an examination:

> I took my SAT exam last week. I know I did really poorly because I wasn't able to finish a bunch of the reading comprehension questions. They give you this passage of three or four paragraphs to read and then you have to answer five multiple-choice questions about what you have just read. Most of them are really dense reading, with lots of details. And the questions are tricky, often hinging on very specific details in the text.
>
> It took me so long on each question! I couldn't remember what I had just finished reading. I would read the passage and then for each question I needed to read it again to find the answer. I had to keep reading this same passage over and over again. I tried reading the questions first so I'd know what details to look for, but by the time I did that and then got back to the paragraphs, I had forgotten the questions. This kind of thing happens to me a lot.

Cluster 6

Action: Monitoring and Self-Regulating Action

In the Action cluster are problems individuals may have in reading social situations and self-regulating their actions. Many people with ADHD, even those without problems of hyperactive behavior, report chronic problems with inhibiting their actions. They often are impulsive in what they say or do and in the way they think, at times jumping too quickly to inaccurate conclusions.

Many also report problems in monitoring the context in which they are interacting. They may fail to notice when other people are puzzled, hurt, or annoyed by what they have just said or done and they fail to modify their behavior in response to specific circumstances. They also report chronic difficulty in regulating the pace of their actions to slow themselves down or speed up as needed for specific tasks. Items in this cluster involve difficulties with interrupting others, being excessively restless, being too fast or too slow, making careless mistakes, or being disruptive to others.

Excessive Restlessness and Impulsivity

One mother expressed concern about her son who had to repeat kindergarten because of his excessive restlessness and impulsivity:

> My son is six years old, but he usually acts like he is only three or four. When he wants something he just goes for it. He just can't wait. He almost got hit by a car last summer because he chased a ball out into the street and didn't even stop to look for oncoming cars. In kindergarten last year he was always in trouble because he grabbed toys or crayons away from other kids.
>
> When they were supposed to sit on the circle and listen for show and tell, he was always interrupting with his own comments; he always had to tell about something he was thinking about. He couldn't wait to listen to another kid or even to the teacher. When he was supposed to draw a picture or copy some shapes, he was always in a hurry. If he tried to do what they asked him to draw or write, he did it too fast and it was too messy.
>
> This year he is repeating kindergarten, but I'm afraid he won't be ready for first grade even next year. He just doesn't seem to be able to slow down enough to listen to the directions or to do anything carefully. He's way behind other kids his age in self-control.

Monitoring Social Interactions

Problems with excessive impulsivity occur not only in children. Many adolescents and adults with ADHD report that they struggle with difficulty regulating their interactions with other people:

> I love getting into intense conversations with other people where it's not just small talk. I love sharing impressions and opinions between people about things that really matter. I think that's how people get to know each other and learn from one another. Usually it works out well, but sometimes I get too intense and turn other people off when I'm trying to find out what they think and why they think that way. Usually I don't notice it at the time; I just see that they drop out of the conversation or walk away.
>
> My wife says I just don't know how to keep my eyes open and notice when others are starting to act bored or frustrated with what's being

discussed. She says that most of the time I talk too much or ask too many questions without noticing how I am coming across and how others are reacting to what I'm saying. She says that most of the time I'm too much mouth and not enough eyes and ears when I'm in a conversation.

Dynamic Interaction of Various Clusters of the ADHD Syndrome Model

Examples listed above illustrate a variety of different ways in which people of different ages struggle with these six clusters of executive function impairments in daily life. However, often these are not separate problems with just one or another cluster. More frequently impairments related to several different clusters merge together within a single conversation fragment or a specific activity. Often they happen quickly and simultaneously in ways not readily noticed. Examples of these various impairments can be found throughout the twelve case examples in this book.

Where in the Brain are Executive Functions?

Executive functions are not really physical parts of the brain, they are patterns of activity in neural networks of the brain that gradually develop from simple patterns to complex, rapidly changing networks that repeatedly redesign themselves in response to whatever situation the person is in, what they see, what they hear, and what they are thinking about. In some ways executive functions are like the colorful patterns of letters and pictures on the huge electrical signs of Times Square in New York City. Yet neural networks are far more complicated than those signs. Executive functions operate in complex three-dimensional networks within the brain that modify and transform rapidly in response to frequently changing experiences and needs of each moment and situation.

The "Central Mystery of ADHD"

The six clusters described above identify characteristics typically problematic for those with ADHD. However, it is important also to understand the "central mystery of ADHD" which is that all those with ADHD tend to have a few specific activities for which they have no difficulty in deploying these executive functions which are problematic for them in almost all other tasks they undertake.

Symptoms of ADHD are chronic, but in each person, they appear with notable exceptions, usually in situations where the person has strong personal interest in a particular task or activity or when they believe that something they consider very unpleasant is likely to occur very quickly if they do not attend to this specific activity right here, right now.

A classic example of this is the situation of Larry, a sturdy, sandy-haired high school junior who was the goalie for his school's ice hockey team. On the day before his parents brought him for an evaluation with me, Larry had helped his team win the state championship in hockey by blocking many shots on goal. He was an extraordinarily fine goalie, and he was also a very bright student who scored in the very superior range on IQ tests.

Larry wanted to get good grades because he was hoping eventually to go to medical school. Yet he was chronically in trouble with his teachers. Often they said to him, "Once a while, you make very perceptive comments in class that show how smart you are, but most of the time you're out to lunch—looking out the window or staring at the ceiling. Occasionally you turn in a really good paper, but most of the time you don't even know what the homework is supposed to be." The teachers kept asking Larry, "If you can pay attention so well when you're playing hockey, why can't you pay attention when you're in class? If you can work so hard to practice and stay in shape for hockey, why can't you show some consistent effort for your schoolwork?"

After hearing his parents tell me about these recurrent complaints from his teachers, Larry quietly responded:

> I don't know why this keeps happening. I'm just as frustrated and even more worried about this than you are … I know what I need to do and I really want to do it because I know how important it is for all the rest of my life … I know I should be able to do it; I but I just can't! I can't make myself pay steady attention to my work for school anywhere near the way I pay attention to hockey.

This inconsistency in motivation and performance is the most puzzling aspect of ADHD. It appears that the child or adult with ADHD who can show strong motivation and focus very well for some tasks should be able to do the same for most other tasks they recognize as important. It appears as if this is a simple problem of lacking "willpower." "If you can do it for this, why can't you do the same for that and that, which are even more important?" However, ADHD is not a matter of willpower. It is a problem with the dynamics of the chemistry of the brain.

One of my patients once told me the following:

> I've got a sexual example for you to show what it's like to have ADHD. It's like having "erectile dysfunction of the mind." If the task you are faced with is something that "turns you on," something that is really interesting to you, you're "up for it" and you can perform. But if the task is not something that's intrinsically interesting to you, if it doesn't turn you on, you can't get up for it and you can't perform. It doesn't matter how much you tell yourself "I need to! I ought to!" It's just not a willpower kind of thing.

(Brown, 2005)

Those specific activities in which persons with ADHD participate without their usual executive function impairments may be playing a sport, reading self-selected books, making music or art, playing video games or some other preferred activities. Occasionally persons with ADHD can demonstrate similar focus, energy and effort for an un-preferred task or activity when they see it as a situation where something they consider very unpleasant will happen quickly if they don't take care of the problem immediately. Such exceptions for strong interest or strong fear can make it appear that ADHD is simply a lack of willpower when, in fact, it is not.

This situational variability of executive function deployment is explained more fully in my earlier books, *Smart but Stuck: Emotions in Teens and Adults with ADHD* (Brown, 2014) and *Outside the Box: Rethinking ADD/ADHD in Children and Adults—A Practical Guide* (Brown, 2017).

How Should ADHD Be Evaluated?

There is no objective laboratory test, brain imaging, or computer test that can validly determine whether a person has or does not have ADHD. Evaluation and diagnosis for ADHD should be made by a trained medical or mental health clinician who is familiar with symptoms of ADHD and the established diagnostic criteria for ADHD. That evaluator should be familiar with executive functions commonly demonstrated in daily life by persons in the age group of the individual being evaluated. The evaluator should also be familiar with other psychological disorders and learning disorders often associated with ADHD.

While some physicians, psychologists and other mental health clinicians are very good at assessment and treatment for ADHD, there are many physicians and mental health practitioners who have had only very limited training and experience for diagnosing and treating those with ADHD, especially for those patients whose ADHD is complicated by other disorders.

The primary tool for assessment of ADHD is a detailed clinical interview with the person being evaluated and with a parent, partner or close friend who can provide adequate information about daily functioning of the person being evaluated. Information about current functioning in school or work, family life and social relationships is essential. Interview inquiry should also include relevant information about health and developmental history, current life stresses, possible co-occurring disorders and other concerns described in references such as Barkley (2006) and Brown (2005, 2017).

Assessment for ADHD should also include a review of the DSM-5 diagnostic criteria for ADHD. However, although those criteria certainly can be helpful and should be considered in making a diagnosis of ADHD, the current DSM-5 diagnostic criteria for ADHD have significant limitations. The primary limitation is that they were developed based on parent and teacher reports of 380 children aged 4 to 16 years and do not provide any research-based norms for anyone over the age of 16. Barkley (2006) has described uses and limitations of the DSM diagnostic criteria for ADHD.

A second limitation is that current DSM criteria for ADHD include few items about executive function impairments. Diagnostic criteria were the best available in 1994 when they were published, but they have many limitations for use now, especially for adolescents and adults. Ronald Kessler at Harvard has done studies on adults which demonstrated that "EF problems are evident in virtually all adults with ADHD" and that "EF symptoms most specifically differentiate adult ADHD from other DSM disorders" (Kessler et al., 2010, p. 1175).

Recent research has also emphasized the importance of utilizing an age-appropriate, normed rating scale in addition to the DSM-5 criteria to assess for executive function impairments of ADHD (Silverstein, Faraone, Leon et al., 2018). Normed rating scales to evaluate for executive functions associated with ADHD are available for all age groups. Examples of such scales include the Barkley Rating Scales (Barkley, 2011a, 2011b, 2011c, 2012a, 2012b, 2012c), the Behavior Rating Inventory of Executive Functions (Gioia et al., 2000; Roth et al., 2005); and the Brown Executive Function/Attention Rating Scales (Brown, 2019).

Computerized assessment measures, brain imaging, or a battery of neuropsychological tests of executive functions are not useful for assessment of ADHD. There was a time when some clinicians believed that assessment of ADHD required a battery of neuropsychological tests. These tests, sometimes referred to by neuropsychologists as "tests of executive function," may be useful for detecting injuries to the brain resulting from traumatic brain injury or a stroke, but they are not helpful in determining how much difficulty a person has in managing activities of daily life such as planning daily activities, organizing tasks, focusing during conversations, preparing a meal or driving a car. More detailed discussion of this issue is available in (Barkley, 2006, 2010, 2012a, 2012b, 2012c; Brown, 2005, 2006, 2013, 2017).

What is the Duration of ADHD Impairments and What Are Likely Outcomes?

To date, the most comprehensive longitudinal study of ADHD was done at Harvard University (Uchida, Spencer, Faraone, and Biederman, 2018). It began with 140 boys and 140 girls diagnosed with ADHD with a comparison sample of 120 boys and 122 girls without ADHD. Participants were followed for an average of 11 years. The mean age at follow-up was 22 years.

At follow-up in young adult years, 77% of the boys and girls initially diagnosed with ADHD continued to display full or subsyndromal ADHD. While only 35% of those ADHD children grown up met full diagnostic criteria for ADHD at follow-up, an additional 43% continued to struggle with some symptoms of ADHD with functional impairment or had reduced symptoms due to their continuing to take ADHD medications. Among the sample, ADHD symptoms of hyperactivity and impulsivity declined earlier on while inattention symptoms tended to persist. These findings were very similar for both the boys and the girls.

Comparisons of the ADHD-diagnosed sample with the control sample indicated ADHD children grown up were significantly more likely to drop out of high school, not to complete college, be jobless, still be financially dependent on their parents, and to attain a lower social class than their parents.

They were also more likely to suffer from not only disruptive behavior disorders; they were also more likely to suffer from mood disorders or anxiety disorders.

These studies documented that children with ADHD who were treated with stimulant medication in childhood were significantly less likely than those with untreated ADHD to be retained in school or to develop mood or anxiety disorders. Stimulant medication treatment for ADHD was also associated with decreased risk during adolescence for negative educational outcomes, or for substance use disorders or additional anxiety or depressive problems. Some who suffer from impairing ADHD during childhood and adolescence eventually manage to function quite well in their adult years, especially if they are provided adequate treatment.

How Are Symptoms of ADHD Related to Development of the Brain?

Imaging studies of brain development in those with ADHD compared to those not affected by ADHD have yielded considerable evidence that ADHD symptoms are related to delays in several different aspects of brain development.

For everyone, the process of brain maturation starts during childhood with rapid proliferation of cells in the large part of the brain near the front that is the headquarters for coordinating the brain's management system. Over years of later childhood and adolescence there is a process in which the brain prunes itself to develop more efficient circuits. Researchers used repeated magnetic resonance imaging (MRI) to study brain development of 223 children diagnosed with ADHD and 223 typically developing children as they were growing up (Shaw et al., 2007).

Results showed no differences between the two groups in maturation of brain structures that process such functions as vision, hearing and movement. However, on average, brains of those with ADHD were 3–5 years slower in maturation of some specific areas of the brain that are important for the brain's cognitive management functions. Other researchers have demonstrated that those with persistent ADHD tend to have similar delays in development of cortical thickness (Wallace et al., 2015), overall brain volume (Hoogman et al., 2017), and development of white matter fibers in the lower part of the brain (Cortesi et al., 2013).

Additional studies have demonstrated that in adults with persistent ADHD there are significant reductions of connectedness between two regions of the brain important for coordinating the brain's management activities. This was not true in those who never had ADHD or in those whose ADHD had gone away (Mattfield et al., 2014).

More details about differences in brain development and brain functioning of those with ADHD are provided in chapter 6 of my book *Outside the Box: Rethinking ADD/ADHD in Children and Adults* (Brown, 2017). However, though brain imaging is a useful way of learning more about the brain processes underlying ADHD, much more remains to be learned. And brain imaging is not, at this time, a useful technique for diagnosing presence or absence of ADHD in individuals.

Selection and "Fine-tuning" of Medication Treatments for ADHD

The most often utilized medications for treatment of ADHD are various versions of methylphenidate and dextroamphetamine. These are available in a variety of long-acting (about 6–10 hours duration of action) and short acting (about 3–6 hours duration of action). Another medication approved by the FDA for treatment of ADHD is guanfacine in an extended-release delivery system. This non-stimulant medication is usually not as effective for improving focus, but it is often more effective than the simulants for reducing hyperactive and/or impulsive ADHD symptoms. Although not officially approved for improving excessive irritability, it often is helpful in reducing irritability in some patients with ADHD. Another non-stimulant medication approved for ADHD is atomoxetine; it is not usually as effective as stimulant medications for improving attention, but for some with ADHD it works when stimulants are not tolerable or effective.

At present there are no medications that can cure ADHD the way antibiotics can cure an infection. Medications approved for treatment of ADHD are more like eyeglasses that can improve a person's vision while they are worn, but the glasses do not fix the person's eyes. Stimulant medications approved for treatment of ADHD are usually helpful to about 8 of 10 children or adults affected, *if those medications are appropriately fine-tuned and monitored.* Fine-tuning to each individual is essential because effective doses of stimulant medications for ADHD are not determined according to how old the person is, how much they weigh, or how severe their ADHD symptoms may be. Effective dose of stimulant medications for ADHD is determined by how sensitive that person's body is to that particular medication. It should be noted that many persons with Asperger syndrome or ASD have an especially sensitive body chemistry which requires very careful fine-tuning of medication choice, timing and dosing (Brown, 2017).

There is considerable evidence that, if appropriately fine-tuned, medication treatments for ADHD can significantly improve executive function impairments of ADHD during the time when the dose of stimulant medication is active in the person's body, but only until that time of day when that medication wears off. For some, improvement from medication is huge; for others improvement is substantial, though not huge; and for some, medication is helpful but not sufficient. And for about two out of ten, it does not do much at all or may cause uncomfortable side effects.

How Can Stimulant Medications be "Fine-tuned" for a Specific Person?

Given the individual variabilities in body sensitivity that influence what dose of stimulant ADHD medication is likely to be most effective and what timing of dosing is likely to provide the best coverage for the individual's daily schedule, careful inquiry is necessary to "fine-tune" for an optimally effective medication regimen. The treating clinician needs to take time to ask not just "How is this medicine working for you?" It is necessary to take the time to ask more detailed questions about specific responses and to link these to time of day.

The first thing is whether the patient has been experiencing any adverse effects, anything that they find uncomfortable or dislike (e.g. headache, stomachache, difficulties with sleep or appetite). If any are reported, it is important to ask when what time of day that problem was noticed, how long it lasted, and when it went away. Was it more in the morning, afternoon or evening? Did it stay the same over the course of the day or did start and then stop? Did this occur only for the first few days of trying this medicine or did it persist and get better or worse over a series of days?

After possible adverse effects are inquired about, it is time to ask whether any benefits or other changes were noticed. This can be done using a scale from 1 to 10 where 1 means that the person was unable to focus and do necessary tasks at all and where 10 means that the person was quite well focused and able to work reasonably well. It is usually helpful to begin by asking where the person would rate himself on that scale if he has had no medication. Once that baseline has been obtained, the clinician can inquire as to where on the scale the person felt at various times in the day (e.g. 8 a.m., 10 a.m., 1 p.m., 4 p.m., 6 p.m. and 8 p.m.).

When linked with information about what doses of medication were taken at particular times of the day, the clinician can develop a profile of how quickly the medication kicks in and at what time it seems to lose effectiveness for that person. This can then be compared with information about times of eating and sleeping and what tasks and demands the person has at various points in the day. By integrating these various bits of information, the clinician can tailor a plan to optimize medication dosing to protect eating and sleeping, and to provide optimal coverage at those times of the day when ADHD medication is needed (Brown, 2017).

What is "Rebound" and How Can One Tell if One's Dose of Medication is too High?

There are three signs that suggest the dose of a stimulant medication may be too high. Each of these applies for the time the medication is supposed to be working and then diminishes as the dose wears off:

1   the person feels "too wired," restless, "revved up" or racey, and then that feeling diminishes as the dose wears off;
2   the person feels much more irritable than usual, annoyed by little frustrations far more than usual; and
3   the person is too serious, loses their "sparkle," their spontaneity; they may be able to focus well, but they are not their regular self.

If any of these patterns occurs over several days during the time the medication is expected to be active, but then diminishes as the medicine wears off, there is a strong probability that the medication dose is too high for that person or that this is just not a good medication for that person.

However, if the person does not have any of those difficulties during the time the medication is expected to be active, and they do have one of those problems later in the day when the medication is expected to be wearing off, that is likely to be a rebound. It does not mean the dose is too high, because that would have been seen during the time the medication was supposed to be active. Instead, such a response during the hours the medication is expected to be wearing off indicates a rebound (Brown, 2017).

"Rebound" is a term to describe the person's "crashing" as the medication is wearing off. Usually this means the medication is dropping off too quickly. Often this can be corrected by administering a small "booster" dose of the short-acting form of that medication about 30 minutes before the rebound has been occurring. This smooths the curve to create a slower, more gradual drop-off from the earlier dose. There are two reasons for using a booster dose. One is to prevent a rebound of excessive restlessness, irritability, or lack of spontaneity. The other use of a booster dose is to extend the duration of the medication's action for a few more hours (Brown, 2017).

How Can You Tell if an ADHD Medication is Working Effectively?

If a stimulant medication is working effectively to alleviate ADHD impairments there should be during the time the medication is active a noticeable improvement in the executive functions described earlier in this chapter Those improvements would be expected to diminish as the medication wears off, just as the vision improvements provided by wearing eyeglasses or contact lenses are lost when the glasses or lenses are removed. Medications do not produce improvements before they actually kick in, a time lag that can be as short as 30 minutes or as long as an hour and a half after taking the pill. If a stimulant medication produces noticeable changes at a given dose level and then, a few days or a week later, does not produce those improvements, it is likely that the dose is almost at the right level, but not quite yet there. A slight increase in dosage should restore the benefits (Brown, 2017).

Some children and adults are very much aware of when their stimulant medication kicks in and when it wears off. Other patients report that they do not feel any different while the medication is supposed to be working, even though parents, teachers, co-workers or friends report that they observe quite a noticeable difference while the medication is active. Sometimes the patient will report that they do not feel any difference in their mood while the medication is in them, but they do notice that they are getting more work done, reading more carefully, or remembering information more easily and consistently than usual. The critical test of the ADHD medication's effectiveness is not so much whether the person feels a dramatic change of mood from it, the test is whether the patient is able to deploy their executive functions more effectively while on medication than they are without the medication.

More detailed information about use of medications for treatment of ADHD is provided in *Straight Talk about Psychiatric Medications for Kids–Fourth Edition* (Wilens and Hammerness, 2016) and in my book, *Outside the Box: Rethinking ADD/ADHD in Children and Adults: A Practical Guide* (Brown, 2017) and in other materials listed in Chapter 17.

Non-Medication Treatments for ADHD

Medications alone are not usually sufficient treatment for ADHD. With or without medication, ongoing education about ADHD is important for those with ADHD and their families so that all can understand what ADHD is and what it is not. It is important to know that ADHD is a highly heritable problem that runs in families and that, contrary to appearances, it is not due to a lack of willpower. It is a problem in the chemistry of the brain. At the same time, it is important to know that ADHD is not an excuse for lack of consistent effort in school, family life, and in work.

Education about ADHD is also important for avoiding false remedies for attentional problems. Many websites advertise ways to treat ADHD using various computer programs or games to "train the brain." Other proposed remedies involve regularly avoiding certain foods (elimination diets) or by consuming various dietary supplements advertised to enhance brain functioning. At present there is no significant scientific evidence that these alternative treatments are effective in alleviating ADHD impairments.

Students who are struggling with ADHD in elementary school, middle school or high school may be eligible for accommodations such as extended time for taking tests, alternative seating, extended time for completion of assignments, or more frequent reports from school to home about work and behavior. Arrangements for such accommodations can be made by parents requesting a meeting with school staff to see if the student may be eligible for accommodations under Federal laws such as Section 504 or the Individuals with Disabilities Education Act.

College students with ADHD can request Section 504 accommodations from the services for students with disabilities office at their college or university. Employed adults with ADHD may be eligible for accommodations at their work under the Americans with Disabilities Act of 1990 or Section 504 of the Rehabilitation Act of 1973 to protect them from discrimination in job assignments, training, promotions, or other working conditions.

For many individuals and families who struggle with ADHD, supportive counseling, cognitive behavioral therapy, psychotherapy, or an ADHD coach may be helpful to deal with a specific crisis or to address ongoing difficulties related to ADHD. Doctors, counselors, and coaches who specialize in such work may be found in listings at the CHADD.org website or in the directory of *ADDitude* magazine (https://directory.additudemag.com). However, unfortunately, many families do not have the money or insurance coverage needed to obtain such help. More detailed information about non-medication treatments for ADHD is available in my book *Outside the Box: Rethinking ADD/ADHD in Children and Adults—A Practical Guide* (Brown, 2017) and in other resources listed in Chapter 17 of this book.

15 Asperger Syndrome

Problems in the Brain's Social-Emotional System

Asperger syndrome is a name for a cluster of characteristics related to social awkwardness and chronic difficulties in understanding one's own and others' feelings and point of view that is found in some children and adults with average or above average intelligence. That syndrome, once a separate diagnosis, was eliminated from the diagnostic manual in 2013 and absorbed into the autism spectrum. This chapter describes Asperger syndrome and advocates for recognizing it as a distinctive syndrome within the autism spectrum.

Dan, the 10-year-old boy described in the introduction of this book, suffered not only from ADHD, he also struggled with social awkwardness and social communication difficulties, especially when interacting with his peers, a problem which we identified as Asperger syndrome. This chapter describes characteristics that comprise the Asperger syndrome.

In 1944 Hans Asperger, an Austrian pediatrician, published a scientific paper about children he had studied who were smart but quite awkward socially. Although this syndrome was included as a specific diagnosis in the official diagnostic manual of the American Psychiatric Association of 1994, it was removed in the 2013 edition of that manual, DSM-5, and subsumed into the diagnosis of Autism Spectrum Disorder. At present, Asperger syndrome is no longer described in the diagnostic manual.

Asperger used the term "autistic" to describe the socially awkward children he studied, but those children were quite different from most of the socially disconnected children described as autistic in early research done in the U.S. and U.K. by Kanner and others. Asperger's children were not so disinterested in relating to others and they did not suffer from low IQ or significant impairments in developing use of language. John Donvan and Caren Zucker described characteristics of the boys studied by Asperger in their book *In a Different Key: The Story of Autism*:

> Most of Asperger's boys ... seemed to strive for connections with others, usually adults, but those relationships were filled with anxiety and were undermined by

DOI: 10.4324/9781003141976-21

the boys' difficult personalities, which did not invite warmth and under-standing. They failed to form relationships with other children, who teased them mercilessly ... Extremely literal-minded, they missed other people's nonverbal signals—the raised eyebrows, the shrugs and sighs, the half-finished sentences ... Most of Asperger's children were extremely verbose ... they spoke more like grown-ups than like their peers, with precise grammar and large vocabularies others found strange or irritating. The boys also tended to lock on to just one or two narrow subjects that fascinated them, and no one else ... their very facility with words undermined their social relations ... despite their difficult experiences with people, most of the boys were more than capable of learning ...

(Donvan and Zucker, 2017, pp. 320–321)

A summary of the syndrome described by Asperger has been provided in the first chapter of *Asperger Syndrome* edited by McPartland, Klin, and Volkmar (2014). They describe these children as having marked difficulties in social interaction despite apparently adequate to excellent cognitive and verbal skills. Those difficulties were manifest in:

1   A "little professor" style of speaking with a tendency to talk at great length about topics of their own interest, while having difficulties with pragmatic aspects of communication such as facial expressions, gestures, voice modulation, and responding to non-verbal cues.
2   Egocentric preoccupation with unusual and circumscribed interests that were the focus of much of the child's life and which precluded other interests more typical of others of similar age.
3   Difficulties in dealing with their feelings, often tending to intellectualize them, while showing little empathy as well as difficulty in understanding social cues.
4   Clumsiness and poor body awareness: inability to participate effectively in group sports because of poor gross motor coordination as well as lacking adequate fine motor coordination resulting in sloppy handwriting.
5   Behavior problems in school due to noncompliance, negativism, and sometimes aggressiveness, much of which resulted from their deficits in social understanding.

Limitations of the DSM-4 diagnostic criteria for Asperger's Disorder have led many clinicians, especially those in Europe and Australia, to utilize the diagnostic criteria for Asperger Syndrome developed by Christopher Gillberg et al. in 2001 (shown below in abbreviated form) rather than the DSM-4 criteria.

1   Social impairment (extreme egocentricity) (at least 2 of the following):

- Difficulties interacting with peers.
- Indifference to peer contacts.
- Difficulties interpreting social cues.

- Socially and emotionally inappropriate behavior.

2   Narrow interest (at least one of the following):

- Exclusion of other activities.
- Repetitive adherence.
- More rote than meaning.

3   Imposition of routines, rituals, and interests (at least one of the following):

- Imposed on others.
- Compulsively followed by self.

4   Speech and language peculiarities (at least three of the following):

- Delayed speech development.
- Superficially perfect expressive language.
- Formal, pedantic speech.
- Odd prosody, peculiar voice characteristics.
- Impairment of comprehension; misinterpretation of literal/implied meanings.

5   Non-verbal communication problems (at least one of the following):

- Limited use of gestures.
- Clumsy/gauche body language.
- Limited facial expression.
- Inappropriate facial expression.
- Peculiar, stiff gaze.

6   Motor clumsiness:

- Poor performance on a neurodevelopmental test.

Steve Silberman's *NeuroTribes: the Legacy of Autism* (2015) includes excerpts from Asperger's writings which noted that some children seen in his clinic had impressive intellectual abilities. He wrote that they

> have the ability to see things and events around them from a new point of view, which often shows surprising maturity. This ability, which remains throughout life, can in favorable cases lead to exceptional achievements which others may never attain. Abstraction ability, for instance, is a pre-requisite for scientific endeavor. Indeed, we find numerous autistic individuals among distinguished scientists.
>
> (Quoted in Silberman, 2015, p. 103)

Asperger also noted that what he was calling autism was not just a disorder of childhood, but a syndrome of characteristics that usually remained persistent throughout the lifespan. He described one of his former patients who had done poorly in school, cared little for his appearance, and seemed so unaware of other people that he failed to recognize acquaintances even when he passed them on the street ... He had barely been able to get through elementary school because of his uncouth behavior, but was spared from expulsion because of his abilities in math. By pleading with his teachers to give him advanced tutoring, he managed to pass the college entrance exam. In his first year at university, he became interested in theoretical astronomy ... he quickly detected an error in one of Newton's proofs. He wrote his dissertation on that subject and became an assistant professor of astronomy at a prestigious university though ... his behavior was extremely clumsy and gauche.

(Quoted in Silberman, 2015, p. 105)

Asperger did not argue that all those with autistic impairments were highly intelligent or likely to become very successful in science or other domains. He wrote that autism

encompasses all levels of ability from the highly original genius, through the weird eccentric who lives in a world of his own and achieves very little ... Autistic individuals are distinguished from each other not only by the degree of contact disturbance and the degree of intellectual ability, but also by their personality and their special interests, which are often outstandingly varied and original

(Quoted in Silberman, 2015, pp. 98–99)

This statement by Asperger provides two important perspectives that are often overlooked in discussions of the syndrome that now bears his name. First, it notes that persons with this syndrome are not all alike, that they vary considerably in their intellectual abilities, in their personalities, and in their special interests. Some with Asperger syndrome emphasize this by saying "When you have met a person with Asperger syndrome you have met just one person with Asperger syndrome." There is no single profile of intellect or personality that is characteristic of all persons with Asperger syndrome!

Second, Asperger's statement highlights the fact that among those with this syndrome are some individuals who are characterized not only by impairments, but also by valuable strengths of intellect and personality as well as special interests and abilities which "are often outstandingly varied and original." Over the years, many with Asperger syndrome have made lasting contributions to various fields of science, mathematics, economics, philosophy, technology, music, drama, art and other fields. Asperger also wrote that "Unfortunately, in the majority of cases, the positive aspects of autism do not outweigh the negative ones" (quoted in Silberman, 2015, p. 104), but this statement needs to be considered in light of the fact that he was describing "cases" in a limited clinical population and not the larger population of those of his time or subsequently that he did not and could not know.

There were three additional differences between the Asperger's observations of autism and those prevailing in the U.S. until decades later. First, he recognized that autism tends to be inherited: "We have been able to discern related incipient traits in parents or relatives in every single case where it was possible for us to make a closer acquaintance" (quoted in Silberman, 2015, p. 99). Second, he asserted that causes of autism are probably not due to any single gene; he argued that this complex set of traits was likely to be polygenetic, due to interactions of multiple genes. And finally, though his research included only males, he acknowledged the possibility that autism could also be found in females:

> While we have never met a girl with the fully fledged picture of autism, we have, however seen several mothers of autistic children whose behavior had decidedly autistic features … It may be only chance that there are no girls among our cases, or it could be that autistic traits in the female become evident only after puberty. We just do not know.
>
> (quoted in Silberman, 2015, p. 99)

Strengths and Difficulties of those with Asperger Syndrome

In thinking about cognitive strengths and difficulties of those with Asperger Syndrome it is important to consider that there are many types of intelligence. Howard Gardner, a professor at Harvard, challenged the notion that humans have just one type of intelligence that can be measured by a single IQ test. In his *Frames of Mind, the Theory of Multiple Intelligences* (Gardner, 1983, 2004) he identified seven different domains of intelligence that operate more or less autonomously. He also claimed that, due to both genetic factors and life experiences, individuals have differences from one another and may differ considerably over their lifetime in terms of their relative strength and weaknesses in each of the intelligences listed below:

- linguistic intelligence;
- spatial intelligence;
- musical intelligence;
- logical-mathematical intelligence;
- body-kinesthetic intelligence;
- interpersonal intelligence; and
- intrapersonal intelligence.

Gardner notes that the interpersonal and intrapersonal intelligences are closely linked and that together these two forms of intelligence shape each individual's unique sense of self:

> intrapersonal intelligence is involved chiefly in an individual's … knowledge of his own feelings while the interpersonal intelligence looks outward

toward behaviors, feelings and motivation of others ... under ordinary circumstances neither form of intelligence can develop without the other. (Gardner, 2011, pp. 232–233)

Persons with Asperger Syndrome tend to be relatively strong in their linguistic, spatial and logical-mathematical intelligences which can have major importance in a variety of academic and technological fields. At the same time those with Asperger Syndrome tend to be relatively weak in their Interpersonal and Intra-personal Intelligence; these social-emotional intelligences are quite important in many aspects of daily social interactions in every culture.

"Systemizing" and "Empathizing"

Another perspective for understanding strengths and difficulties of those with Asperger syndrome was proposed by Simon Baron-Cohen, director of the Autism Research Centre at Cambridge University. In his 2003 book *The Essential Difference*, Baron-Cohen proposed a theory for understanding autistic traits in terms of contrasting stereotypes of male and female cognitive styles. He claimed that those with Asperger syndrome tend to have a unique cognitive style which is quite biased toward an emotionally detached, intellectually abstract, analytic approach to looking at the world and other persons. In some ways this biased style is a strength for them, while in other ways their biased style impairs their social development and interpersonal interactions.

Baron-Cohen described this biased style as an extreme "systemizing" approach in which one is driven to analyze, explore and construct a system. The systemizer intuitively figures out how things work, or extracts rules that govern the behavior of a system. This is done in order to understand and predict the system or to invent a new system (Baron-Cohen, 2003, p. 3). This he characterized as an extreme of the stereotype of the "male brain." He notes that this style is useful in understanding many objects, processes and events, but is not helpful in under-standing day-to-day interactions with other people.

In contrast, Baron-Cohen (2003) describes the extreme stereotype of the "female brain" as "hardwired for empathy," driven by efforts to "identify another's emotions and to respond to them with an appropriate emotion." He emphasizes that this empathy is not the cold, detached calculation of what another person thinks or feels such as is characteristic of a psychopath. Rather, he notes that "empathizing occurs when we feel an appropriate emotional reaction, an emotion triggered by another person's emotion and it is done in order to understand another person, to predict their behavior, and to connect or resonate with them emotionally" (p. 2).

Baron-Cohen argues that systemizing and empathizing are wholly different kinds of processes.

You use one process—empathizing—for making sense of an individual's behavior, and you use the other—systemizing—for predicting almost everything else. To systemize you use detachment in order to monitor information and track which factors cause information to vary. To empathize you need some degree of attachment in order to recognize that you are interacting with a person, not an object, but a person with feelings and whose feelings affect your own.

(Baron-Cohen, 2003, p.5)

In his model Baron-Cohen claims that all of us have both systemizing and empathizing skills, but that individuals vary from one another in how much they are oriented more one way or the other. His view is that while most persons are generally balanced in these two different cognitive styles, those with Asperger syndrome are usually characterized by dominant strength in systemizing and relatively weak abilities in empathizing. They may be extremely logical and rational, but they are not usually strong in understanding emotional or psychological interactions. These theories have been supported in research that involved more than half a million people including 36,000 autistic people (Greenberg, Warrier, Allison, and Baron-Cohen, 2018).

According to Baron-Cohen "ultimately systemizing and empathizing depend on independent sets of regions in the human brain … they are grounded in our neurophysiology" (Baron-Cohen, 2003, p. 6). He also suggests that these traits tend to have a genetic basis, that they run in families. He notes that there are higher rates of autism and Asperger syndrome in families of those talented in math, physics and engineering compared to those talented in the humanities.

"Emotional Intelligence"

Another way of thinking about the limitations of those with Asperger syndrome is that they have more limited "emotional intelligence." In 1990 psychologists Peter Salovey and John Mayer published a journal article titled "Emotional Intelligence" which elaborated on the domain Gardner referred to as "the personal intelligences" (interpersonal and intrapersonal). In that paper they defined emotional intelligence as "the ability to monitor one's own and others' feelings and emotions and to use this information to guide one's thinking and actions" (Salovey and Mayer, 1990). Although research on emotional intelligence did not extend to study of those abilities in persons with Asperger syndrome, rating scale items designed to measure emotional intelligence clearly involve skills that tend to be relatively weak in persons with Asperger syndrome.

Decades earlier in psychology the term "alexithymia" was used to describe lack of emotional intelligence in adults. Alexithymia is a Greek word which translates as "a lack of words for feelings and emotions." This term was used by some psychologists and psychiatrists in the late twentieth century, most of them psychoanalysts, to describe a syndrome of difficulties they found in patients with psychosomatic problems, eating disorders, post-traumatic stress disorders, and substance use disorders (Taylor and Bagby, in Bar-On, Parker, and Goleman, 2000).

The alexithymia syndrome includes chronic difficulty in identifying one's own feelings and in describing those feelings to others; it is also related to difficulties in identifying emotions in the faces of others, limited capacity for empathizing, and difficulty in recalling dreams. Interestingly, with just a couple of exceptions (e.g. Fitzgerald and Bellgrove, 2006), similarities between alexithymia and Asperger syndrome or autism have not been recognized or studied. It seems likely that many of the adult patients identified in earlier days as suffering from alexithymia might be seen in current days as being adults with Asperger syndrome.

Atypical Sensory Processing in Persons with Asperger Syndrome

Most studies and discussions of strengths and difficulties of those with Asperger syndrome focus only on cognitive and social functioning. Yet for decades Temple Grandin and now recent research have highlighted atypical sensory processing as an important, often problematic, aspect of life for individuals with Asperger syndrome. She claims that nine out of ten people with autism, including high functioning persons like herself, suffer from one or more sensory disorders (Grandin, 2014, p. 71). She wrote:

> For me and other people on the autism spectrum, sensory experiences that have little or no effect on neurotypical people can be severe life stressors for us ... Loud noises hurt my ears like a dentist's drill hitting a nerve ... For some individuals, seams in a pair of socks or the rough texture of materials like wool can feel like being constantly burned ... For others, even the light touch of another's hand on their arm can be painful ... like razors drawn across their skin.
>
> (Grandin, 2014, p. 102)

Grandin also notes:

> sensory sensitivities are very variable, among individuals and within the same individual. A person can by hypersensitive in one area (like hearing) and hyposensitive in another (like touch) ... Complicating matters even further, on a day-to-day basis, in the same individual, sensory sensitivities can change, especially when the person is tired or stressed.
>
> (Grandin, 2014, p. 103)

These sensitivities may appear transient and trivial to those who have not experienced them, but Grandin reports:

> Auditory challenges are often the #1 sensory challenge among individuals with autism/Asperger's. There are two kinds: (1) sensitivity to loud noise in general and (2) not being able to hear auditory detail, such as discerning one voice among other sounds, or hearing the hard consonant sounds of

words … Sound sensitivity can make it *impossible* for some people on the spectrum to tolerate normal places such as restaurants, offices and sports events … [even for] those who are very high functioning with marked intelligence and language abilities, such as educated people with Asperger's.

(Grandin, 2014, p. 106)

Over the past decade, the broader scope of the three types of atypical sensory processing: hyper-responsiveness, hypo-responsiveness, and sensory seeking has been shown to have significant impact upon language, communication, and social functioning of those on the autism spectrum. Examples include difficulty in processing emotion implicit in others' speech, facial movements or bodily movements and difficulty in filtering out background noise to listen to what others are saying., Hypersensitivity of neural circuits can cause perceptual up-regulation of sensory information which can lead to avoidance of emotional cues from eyes or facial expressions and social avoidance. Hyposensitivity to sensory stimuli can result in lack of appropriate response and poor multi-sensory integration which impairs social communication (Thye et al., 2018).

How Many Individuals Have Asperger Syndrome?

At present it is virtually impossible to get an accurate estimate of how many people in the general population have Asperger Syndrome. The primary problem is that current data from the U.S. Centers for Disease Control (CDC) are based solely on counting only young children diagnosed with autism spectrum. A related problem is that the current count does not differentiate adequately between types or levels of impairment.

Over the past decade a rapidly increasing number of children have been diagnosed as bring on the autism spectrum, often referred to simply as "the spectrum." In 2008 the U.S. Centers for Disease Control estimated that 1 in 125 children was diagnosed as being on this spectrum; in 2018 the estimated number of children on the spectrum jumped to 1 in 59.

The major problem with those CDC estimates is that they are based solely upon the number of children diagnosed with autism by the age of 8 years. More than 50% of children diagnosed with autism by that early age suffer from significant intellectual disabilities and serious delays in their development of language as well as substantial impairments in their ability for social interaction and social communication. Many children with autistic characteristics and average or higher than average IQ are not identified until long after their 8th birthday, often not until middle school where they encounter challenges of increased peer interaction and less direct adult supervision. Some are not diagnosed until their adult years. It is likely that most of those with autistic symptoms not complicated by intellectual disability are not included in the CDC count. It is probable that a much larger number of individuals would be included in the estimated prevalence if it included those not identified until later childhood or beyond.

Most attention to the Autism Spectrum has been focused primarily on children under 8 years, many of whom have severe delays in developing language skills and IQ scores in the low average to intellectually disabled range. Relatively little clinical or research attention has been given to the much larger number of those on the Autism Spectrum who have average or above average IQ and adequate or precocious language skills. These individuals often are not recognized, diagnosed and provided any assistance until they are in adolescence or adulthood, if at all.

Current research estimates that about 32% of those diagnosed with autism spectrum disorder (ASD) are intellectually disabled while about 24% have IQ estimated in the borderline intellectually disabled range. It is estimated that about 44% of those with an autism spectrum diagnosis have IQ in the average or above average range (Christensen et al. quoted in Volkmar, 2019). Given the problems in ascertainment mentioned above, and including adults it is likely that the actual number of persons who would meet diagnostic criteria for Asperger Syndrome is probably substantially larger than current estimates.

IQ Alone is Not an Adequate Indicator of How Persons with Autism Can Function in Daily Life

Often the term "high-functioning" is used to describe individuals with ASD who do not have intellectual disability. Those "high-functioning" individuals with IQ of 70 or higher are generally assumed to have stronger skills for daily life and better long-term outcomes. However, clinical observations have found that often this is not true. A 2019 study of over 2000 children registered in Australia as on the autism spectrum compared those with intellectual disability at the time of their diagnosis with those whose IQ was 70 or above when they were diagnosed. Both groups were evaluated with a measure of daily functioning, the Vineland Adaptive Behavior Scale, a well-normed measure of everyday functioning (Alvares et al., 2019).

Results showed that those with intellectual disability tended to demonstrate daily adaptive functioning that was generally close to their relatively low IQ scores, while those with higher IQ, as they grew older, tended to have an increasingly wider gap between their relatively stronger IQ scores and their everyday functioning scores. This led the researchers to conclude that the term "high functioning autism" is an inaccurate clinical descriptor when based solely upon IQ scores.

From these results the researchers urged that assessment of those on the autism spectrum should take into account not just IQ scores, but also other factors that impact everyday functioning such as language development and other complicating factors. This more comprehensive approach to assessment and identifying strengths and limitations is much more likely to provide a solid basis for designing interventions that help to improve daily functioning than is an assessment based solely on IQ scores.

Lack of Social Motivation Is Not Characteristic of All on the Autism Spectrum

Often it is assumed that persons with autism have little or no social interest, that they prefer to be left alone, that they are uninterested in social interaction because they often do not maintain eye contact or show interest in what others are looking at, saying or doing. This assumption has been challenged in a 2019 article by Jaswal and Akhtar who questioned a variety of people on the autism spectrum and provided alternative explanations for the persistent tendencies of many of those on the autism spectrum to keep their distance from others much of the time.

The argument presented in that paper suggests that for many, not necessarily all, on the autism spectrum, their apparent lack of motivation for social interaction with others may be more a problem of lacking sufficient understanding and skills needed for social interactions than it is a lack of interest or desire for interacting with others. This is quite consistent with statements by the four smart and successful adults with ADHD and Asperger syndrome quoted in Chapter 1 of this book. For example, John Robison wrote in his autobiography:

> Many descriptions of autism and Asperger's describe people like me as "not wanting contact with others" or "preferring to play alone." I can't speak for other kids … but I did not ever want to be alone … I played by myself because I was a failure at playing with others. I was alone as a result of my own limitations …
>
> (Robison, 2008, p. 211)

Also quoted in Chapter 1 of this book, Cynthia Kim wrote:

> When you arrive in adulthood lacking the social skills that most people have mastered by sixth grade, life becomes exponentially more confusing and hard to navigate … Typical people acquire social skills mainly by absorption … we need to be taught social skills explicitly.
>
> (Kim, 2015, pp. 32–34)

The article by Jaswal and Akhtar draws attention to a variety of possible explanations for why many on the autism spectrum may appear unmotivated for social interactions while, in fact, they may simply lack the requisite skills and find it difficult to acquire them. Their paper has elicited considerable discussion from other experts who support or provide other ways to interpret their data. Many of these thoughtful responses were published with the original journal article.

How Persistent Are Impairments of Asperger Syndrome?

Several studies have demonstrated that many individuals who meet diagnostic criteria for an ASD during childhood do not continue to persist with the same level of autistic impairments throughout their lifetime. One large research project involving 405 individuals found large improvements (retrospectively assessed) across multiple domains in the current functioning of adolescents and adults who had been diagnosed with autism spectrum as children. Their current functioning scores indicated that only about half of the sample met full criteria for Autistic Disorder while about 11% no longer met diagnostic criteria for any diagnosis on the autism spectrum (Seltzer, Lord, Swe et al., 2003).

This is consistent with an earlier review of follow-up studies which reported that "the natural course of autism is gradual symptomatic improvement with persistent, residual social impairments" (Rumsey, Rapoport, and Sceery, 1985). Yet, clinical experience indicates that often those "persistent, residual social impairments" however improved, may involve significant social, educational and financial impairments that can be quite difficult, stressful and painful for affected individuals and their families.

One nationally representative study of postsecondary education and employment in youth 19 to 23 years old with an ASD compared them with others of similar age in three other disability categories: speech/language impairment; learning disability; and intellectual disability. All participants had received special education services while in high school. Results showed that among youth with an ASD 34% had attended either a 2-year or 4-year college and 55% had held paid employment at some time during the first six years after high school. Of those with an ASD, more than 50% of those who had left high school in the previous two years had no participation in employment or education (Shattuck, Narendorf, Cooper et al., 2012).

That study showed that youth with an ASD had the lowest rates of participation in employment compared to youth in the other three disability categories and the highest rates of no participation in further education except for those in the intellectual disability group. Those with higher income families and better functional abilities had better odds of participation in post-secondary employment and education. Authors of that study concluded their report by observing:

> youth with an ASD are uniquely at high risk for a period of struggling to find ways to participate in work and school after leaving high school. These findings point to potential gaps in transition planning specifically for youth with autism and barriers to participation that may be specific to this population.
>
> (Shattuck et al., 2012, p. 1047)

Another study of youth employment after high school reported that while 58% of those on the autism spectrum had worked during their early twenties, over 90% of young adults with emotional disturbance, speech/language impairment, or learning disability had work experience after high school (Roux, Shattuck, Rast et al., 2015). Nearly 42% of those young adults on the autism spectrum never worked for pay during their early 20s. In analyzing those data, researchers identified four factors affecting those findings:

- Conversation ability: Nearly 90% of those with highest level of conversation skills ever worked, compared to 15% with the lowest conversation skills level.
- Work experience: Employment rate was over twice as high for those who worked for pay during high school (90%) versus those who did not (40%).
- Race and Ethnicity: Twice as many white young adults (66%) were employed compared to black and Hispanic young adults (37% and 34% respectively).
- Household Income: Nearly 72% of those from upper income households (over $75,000) ever worked after high school compared to 33% of those from lowest income households (less than $25,000) (Roux, Shattuck, Rast et al., 2015).

It is important to note that these two studies of postsecondary education and employment are reporting on students who had been provided special education services in high school. While some with Asperger syndrome receive special education services in high school, many do not have need for those services. For those who have stronger conversational abilities, especially if they also have the advantage of more substantial family income and do not face the bias of racial prejudice, pursuing post-secondary education and employment is likely to be less problematic, but clinical experience and examples in this book suggest that even for students with Asperger syndrome and ADHD who have strong cognitive abilities and considerable family support, transitions into college or university and into employment can be quite challenging.

At present, few studies provide specific information about how those with Asperger syndrome fare with education following their completion of high school. One exception is a report by Gelbar, Shefcyk, and Reichow (2015) who surveyed 35 college students or recent college graduates most of whom reported having been diagnosed with Asperger syndrome. The average GPA was 3.27. Most reported academic success despite some difficulty with executive function skills and with navigating their campus social environment. Most also reported receiving helpful support and accommodations from their campus services for students with disabilities.

Is Asperger Syndrome a Distinct Category Totally Separate from Autism?

Population-based research studies have found that many people have autistic-like traits, but not the full syndrome of Autism or Asperger syndrome. A research study tried to answer the question of whether those with the full syndrome of Autism constitute a distinct category with its own causes or whether persons with Asperger-like traits such as problems or peculiarities in social communication, perceptions of self and others, and functioning in social environments have a similar problem with totally different genetic causes (Lundström, Chang, Rostam et al. 2012).

To answer this question those researchers studied genetic profiles in 9- to 12-year-old children with autism or autism-like traits (ALTS) in a nationwide sample of 3,400 pairs of twins in Sweden. Results indicated that genetics underlying ASD are not significantly different from those in the general population who have autism-like traits, but not the full syndrome of Autism.

Given that genetic characteristics of those with autism-like traits like Asperger syndrome and those with the full syndrome of autism are genetically linked, it is not unreasonable to include Asperger syndrome in the autism spectrum. However, the significant differences, especially the differences in intelligence and language abilities, between those with Asperger syndrome and others on the autism spectrum who are much more impaired in language and intelligence certainly seems to warrant a distinctive diagnostic category for Asperger syndrome within the autism spectrum. It is important to recognize both the similarities and the differences between those with Asperger syndrome and those on the autism spectrum who are much more severely impaired. The ecological context and needs of those two groups are quite different.

Researchers in the field have emphasized that differences in verbal IQ and current language skills of those on the autism spectrum need to be taken into account and that to provide effective treatment and support for those on the spectrum it is important to identify subgroups within the autism spectrum (Lai, Lombardo, Chakrabarti, and Baron-Cohen, 2013).

Why Refer to this Cluster of Characteristics as Asperger Syndrome?

It is not uncommon in fields of medicine to refer to a particular syndrome using the name of the first researcher to publish a description of that syndrome. In recent years some have argued that the name of Asperger should not be used to refer to the syndrome he was the first to describe. Having read historical research indicating that Asperger was probably involved in collaborating with Nazi policies in Austria when they were sending some disabled children to settings where some were deliberately killed, some argue that Asperger's name should not be used to identify the syndrome he was first to describe. In our clinic we continue to use the non-possessive form of the name Asperger to describe that syndrome. Our reason is that for several decades many individuals have proudly described themselves as having Asperger syndrome or as "Aspies." We feel that there is no need to deprive them of using that recognized label for their syndrome. Even researchers who urged removing the separate diagnosis for Asperger syndrome from the DSM have noted that there is no reason that advocacy groups cannot continue to use the term Asperger to identify their groups or that individuals should refrain from identifying themselves as having Asperger syndrome (Lord and Jones, 2012).

How Should Asperger Syndrome be Evaluated?

As in the case of ADHD, there is no objective laboratory test, brain imaging, or computer test that can validly determine whether a person has or does not have Asperger syndrome. Moreover, at present, Asperger syndrome is not an official diagnosis in the current version of the DSM-5. As was explained previously in this chapter, those with characteristics of Asperger syndrome are currently supposed to be diagnosed simply as being on the autism spectrum.

As mentioned earlier, there are reasons from genetic similarities that warrant including those with Asperger syndrome on the autism spectrum. However, I believe that if those with Asperger syndrome are to be included on the spectrum, there ought to be a distinctive set of diagnostic criteria to clarify how those with this syndrome are different from most others on the autism spectrum, despite some similarities.

The primary difference between those with Asperger syndrome and others on the autism spectrum is that those with Asperger syndrome have at least average development of language skills for their age and have IQ in the average or above average range. This is not the same as saying that those with Asperger syndrome are "higher functioning" than others on the autism spectrum. As noted in earlier pages of this chapter, there is evidence that having high IQ does not necessarily equate to strong global functioning in activities of daily life. In fact, as is shown in the 12 cases described in this book, those with Asperger syndrome often have impairments in emotional and social communication that significantly impair them in many aspects of daily life.

Although DSM-5 does not include Asperger syndrome, the diagnostic criteria for Asperger syndrome provided by DSM-4 can be useful for assessment of Asperger syndrome so long as the evaluator notes that not every symptom listed in those diagnostic criteria needs to be present. The criteria themselves require only "at least two" of the listed symptoms of impairments in social interactions and only "at least one" of the listed symptoms of repetitive and stereotyped patterns of behavior, interests and activities. The most important of the DSM-4 diagnostic criteria for Asperger syndrome is item C: "the disturbance causes clinically significant impairment in social, occupational or other areas of functioning."

DSM-4 diagnostic criteria also stipulate that diagnosis for Asperger syndrome also should include "no clinically significant delay in language" and "no clinically significant delay in cognitive development or in the development of age-appropriate self-help skills, adaptive behavior (other than in social interaction), and in curiosity about the environment in childhood" (American Psychiatric Association, 2000, p. 84). Diagnostic criteria from DSM-4 might be improved, but they are certainly an adequate beginning for differentiating those with Asperger syndrome from others on the Autism spectrum and from those lacking significant autistic traits.

In the present time, if DSM-4 diagnostic criteria are to be utilized for an "unofficial" diagnosis of Asperger syndrome as they are in our clinic, the person making the assessment should be a medical or mental health clinician familiar with both the established diagnostic criteria for ASD and with the DSM-4 diagnostic criteria for Asperger syndrome. That evaluator should be also be familiar with ADHD diagnostic criteria and with the range of executive functions commonly demonstrated in daily life by persons in the age group of the individual being evaluated. In addition, the evaluator should be familiar with other cognitive, behavioral, emotional, and learning disorders often associated with Asperger syndrome and with ADHD.

While some physicians, psychologists and other mental health clinicians are quite competent at assessment and treatment for ADHD and Asperger syndrome, there are many physicians and mental health practitioners who have had very limited or no training or experience in diagnosing and treating children, adolescents or adults on the Autism spectrum. This gap in medical training was noted by McDougle as he noted the rapidly increasing prevalence of ASD:

> Many medical providers who care for typical adults have never evaluated or treated an individual with autism in their career … it may be time to require comprehensive didactic learning and clinical rotations on developmental disabilities including autism, across the lifespan for medical students and residents.
>
> (McDougle, 2013, pp. 566–568)

The same deficit exists in professional training of most psychologists and other mental health professionals.

The primary tool for assessment of Asperger syndrome is a detailed clinical interview with the person being evaluated and with a parent, partner or close friend who can provide adequate information about daily functioning of the person being evaluated. Information about current functioning in school or work, family life and social relationships is essential. Interview inquiry should also include relevant information about health and developmental history, current life stresses, possible co-occurring disorders and other concerns described in references listed below.

Assessment for Asperger syndrome should include not only a review of the DSM-4 diagnostic criteria for Asperger syndrome, but also use of a normed rating scale for Asperger syndrome. In our clinic we usually utilize the *Social Responsiveness Scale-Second Edition* (SRS-2) by Constantino and Gruber (2012) in evaluations for possible Asperger syndrome in children, adolescents, and adults. The 65 items of that questionnaire can be administered in about 15–20 minutes; they cover social awareness, social cognition, social communication, social motivation, as well as restricted interests and repetitive behavior. The SRS-2 has forms appropriate for use with preschool children (up to 4 years), school age (4 to 18 years) and adults (19 years and up).

An alternative rating scale specifically for adults is the *Ritvo Autism Asperger Diagnostic Scale-Revised* by Ritvo, Ritvo, Guthrie et al. (2010). It is designed for diagnosis of Asperger syndrome or ASD in adults 18 years or older with average or above average intelligence; it reports four factors: social relatedness, circum-scribed interests, sensory motor, and social anxiety. Another alternative rating scale designed specifically for women aged between 18 and 72 is the modified Girls Questionnaire for Autism Spectrum Condition which reports five factors: (1) Imagination and Play; (2) Camouflaging; (3) Sensory sensitivities; (4) Socializing; and (5) Interests. It has been shown to be an effective and highly discriminant screening tool for use with adult autistic women (Brown, Attwood, Garnett, and Stokes, 2020). It should be noted that unless (or until) the DSM and ICD diagnostic manuals are revised to include diagnosis of Asperger Syndrome as an officially recognized disorder within ASD, insurance coverage for this syndrome will depend upon the current diagnostic criteria for ASD. Diagnosis of Asperger syndrome can be utilized as an educational tool for helping patients and their family to understand the syndrome and may be included in psychological reports, but a diagnosis of Asperger syndrome is not likely to be recognized as a basis for insurance reimbursement.

Medication Treatments for Those with Asperger Syndrome

Currently there are no medications officially approved for treatment of Asperger syndrome or ASD. The only exceptions are two atypical antipsychotics: risperidone and aripiprazole, both of which have been approved by the FDA for treatment of irritability and agitation in children with ASD. However, many individuals with Asperger syndrome or other diagnoses within the autism spectrum are treated with medications targeted to address specific symptoms that often impair those with Asperger syndrome or others on the autism spectrum.

Mahajan et al. (2012) published a review of medication choice for ADHD symptoms in ASD. That review, developed by a committee of clinical specialists affiliated with Autism Speaks, noted that ADHD symptoms occur in 41% to 78% in large samples of children on the autism spectrum (ASD). The report reviewed and evaluated more than 1200 research studies on various medications used for treatment of ADHD and related symptoms in children with ASD. These included stimulant medications such as various methylphenidate and amphetamine products; Alpha agonists such as guanfacine and clonidine; atypical anti-psychotics such as Risperidone and Aripiprazole; atomoxetine and nortriptyline.

Based on these research data, the report recommended stimulant medications, methylphenidate or amphetamines, as first line for treatment of ADHD symptoms in children with ASD, though they also noted that side effects are more common with those children and the effectiveness, as shown in controlled studies, is not as strong as for typical children with ADHD. The study also reported that Risperidone and Aripiprazole had the most evidence for efficacy in treating irritability or agitation sometimes associated with ADHD in ASD children. However, they also noted that those two medications often have more significant adverse effects such as weight gain/metabolic disorder and sometimes movement disorders.

Guanfacine and clonidine were described in the Mahajan et al. (2012) report as frequently used for treatment of ADHD symptoms in children with

ASD, either as single medications or in combination with stimulants for treatment of ADHD. The report noted that guanfacine tends to be longer-lasting and less sedating than clonidine and that there were only open-label studies of those two agents at that time.

Subsequent to the Mahajan report a significant controlled study of extended release Guanfacine for treatment of ADHD symptoms in patients with Autism Spectrum Disorder was reported by clinicians from the Research Units on Pediatric Psychopharmacology Autism Network (Scahill et al., 2015). Findings indicated that extended release guanfacine appeared to be safe and effective for reducing hyperactivity, impulsiveness, and distractibility in children with Autism Spectrum Disorder and ADHD. Another study by the same team reported that parent ratings of oppositional behavior declined 44% on guanfacine extended release vs. 12% on placebo for children with both ASD and ADHD while repetitive behavior declined 24% vs 1% on placebo (Politte et al., 2018). Another well-controlled study on use of guanfacine for adolescents with ADHD (Wilens et al., 2015) reported similar findings, but that study did not include patients who also had ASD.

There have been few studies of atomoxetine for treatment of children with ASD and ADHD. One study reported on 128 children (ages 5 to 14 years) treated with atomoxetine in combination with a program of 9 sessions of parent training (Handen et al., 2015). For oppositional symptoms atomoxetine with and without parent training was superior to placebo; the medication was well tolerated, and authors concluded atomoxetine might be a viable alternative to stimulant medications for youth with ASD despite its lower efficacy.

Often children on the autism spectrum are treated with more than one medication at a time. One study by Logan et al. (2015) found that 60% of a sample of 675 children diagnosed with ASD had been treated with at least one psychotropic medication while 41% of the 675 were treated with two or more such medications. Researchers found that autistic children with argumentative, hyperactive/impulsive behavior, self-injurious behaviors or a co-occurring diagnosis of ADHD, anxiety or mood disorder, or conduct/oppositional defiant disorder were more likely to be treated with more than one medication.

A large nationally representative study of adolescents 13–17 years old who had both ASD and ADHD yielded a very similar percentage of 58% being given at least one medication while the proportion of those adolescents with only ASD was 34% and the proportion for those with only ADHD was 49% (Frazier et al., 2011). The most commonly prescribed medication for those with both ASD and ADHD was a stimulant (57%). Prevalence of other medication types for those with both disorders was 40% for anti-psychotic medications, 51% for anti-depressants, 33% for SSRI, and 18% for mood stabilizers. That report noted the need for more clear practice parameters to guide clinicians who are treating those with complex combinations of impairments.

Most of the reported trials of medication treatments for ADHD and for ASD are of relatively short duration, usually less than 3 months. One exception is a recently published naturalistic study of 40 children and adolescents with ASD and co-occurring ADHD compared with a group of 40 children and adolescents with ADHD only (Ventura et al., 2020). Both groups were treated consistently with methylphenidate and monitored for safety and effectiveness for terms which lasted from 6 to 156 months (longer than 24 months in more than three quarters of the patients).

In the group with both ASD and ADHD many had co-occurring disorders: 78% learning disorder; 27% motor coordination disorder; 25% sleep-wake disorder; 23% anxiety disorder; 15% oppositional defiant disorder; and 13% disruptive mood regulation disorder. IQ range was 84–102, with a median of 90. Results indicated that methylphenidate was associated with reduction in illness severity and overall improvement in functioning. The medication was effective and well-tolerated in children and adolescents with both ASD and ADHD just as well as it was in those with ADHD without ASD. This finding challenges reports of earlier years that found this medication less effective and causing more adverse effects than in those with ADHD only.

More detailed information about use of medications for treatment of ADHD and Asperger syndrome is available in *Straight Talk About Psychiatric Medications for Kids* (Wilens and Hammerness, 2016); *Parent's Guide to the Medical World of Autism* (Aull, 2013); and my book, *Outside the Box: Rethinking ADD/ADHD in Children and Adults—A Practical Guide* (Brown, 2017).

Non-Medication Treatments for ADHD with Asperger Syndrome

Generally, medications alone are not sufficient treatments for ADHD with Asperger syndrome. Usually education about both ADHD and Asperger syndrome is important for those affected as well as for their families. However many with Asperger syndrome need personalized education about social interactions. Useful tools for such individualized tutoring about social skills are *The Social Skills Picture Book* (2001), *The Social Skills Picture Book for High School and Beyond* (2006), *Preparing for Life* (2005), and *No More Meltdowns* (2008), all by Jed Baker.

Individuals with Asperger syndrome, with or without ADHD, often need help from parents, teachers, counselors, or therapists in understanding social situations that arise in their daily interactions with others. They may think quite logically about social interactions, but it is not easy for them to think psychologically about their interactions with others. They often find it difficult to see why others feel hurt or annoyed if they make comments that are critical of another person, perhaps regarding the person's appearance or something they have said or done.

For example, a ninth grade student, Fred, came to his scheduled psychotherapy session with me complaining that several of his classmates had been repeatedly throwing pieces of their sandwiches at him during lunch period that day and had been laughing at him for no reason. I asked him to tell me about any interactions he had with them earlier that day. He mentioned that he had heard those three boys talking about the final exam that he and they had completed just before lunch. Those three boys had been complaining that the exam was very difficult despite their having studied intensively for it. They mentioned that they had studied for the exam for many hours on the two preceding days and nights, yet they had been unable to answer many of the questions. They felt the exam was too hard and they were afraid that they would be failing the exam.

Fred reported he had simply told them that he had found the exam really easy even though he had not studied for it at all and that he had been able to answer all of the questions on the test. He did not see why that would bother them because he was just telling them the truth. It took a while for me to help him understand how his comment probably embarrassed and annoyed them. This is one simple example of how people with Asperger syndrome find it difficult to size up and navigate social interactions, especially with their peers. Repeated experiences of such misunderstanding can establish patterns where they unwittingly provoke peers to bully them.

In addition to such individualized tutoring about social interaction problems as they arise, many adolescents and young adults can also benefit from group social skills programs. One example is the PEERS program developed by Elizabeth Laugeson at UCLA. That program has been adopted in many schools and clinics throughout the U.S. and internationally. Manuals and information about that program are described in Chapter 17 of this book.

More detailed information about non-medication treatments for ADHD is available in my book *Outside the Box: Rethinking ADD/ADHD in Children and Adults— A Practical Guide* (Brown, 2017) and in other resources listed in Chapter 17.

Additional resources for assessment and treatment of Asperger syndrome and ASD are available in the *Essential Clinical Guide to Understanding and Treating Autism* (Volkmar and Wiesner, 2018), *Asperger Syndrome* (McPartland, Klin, and Volkmar, 2014) and *Psychiatry of Adult Autism and Asperger Syndrome* (Brugha, 2018).

16 Overlap and Complications on Complications

I grew up in the city of Chicago. Several times each year my parents, my sister, and I would drive from Chicago to visit my paternal grandfather in the small town in Iowa where he and other relatives lived. Driving through the farmland of Iowa I saw that many farms had a silo, a very tall circular structure with a pointed top that towered over the wide fields, the barn, and the farmhouse. I learned that silos are used to store large quantities of grain.

In the field of medicine, diagnostic "silos" have been developed to describe symptoms that characterize each particular disorder. These diagnostic silos are helpful for recognizing clusters of symptoms that often appear together in a particular disorder and in differentiating one disorder from another. However, diagnoses describe clusters of symptoms; they do not describe an individual person experiencing a particular disorder. Often a person with one disorder also has some, if not all, symptoms of one or more additional disorders which may strongly affect how they experience their difficulties, which treatments they need, and how they respond to treatment.

Unfortunately, some medical and mental health professionals often focus on one diagnosis that may seem to fit a person while overlooking or ignoring symptoms that may be less obvious, but are concurrently impairing that individual and may be significantly complicating the person's functioning and response to treatment. This often happens to persons who have ADHD as well as characteristics of Asperger syndrome and also with children or adults recognized as having Asperger syndrome while also having symptoms of ADHD which remain unrecognized.

Until the release of DSM-5 in 2013, DSM criteria prohibited diagnosis of ADHD in individuals diagnosed with an autism spectrum disorder. That restriction was lifted because various research studies and clinical experience in treatment of persons on the Autism spectrum had shown not only that many on the autism spectrum are impaired by ADHD and related executive function impairments. It had also been found that having ADHD symptoms concurrent to Autism spectrum disorder significantly diminishes adaptive functioning. Additionally it had been shown that adequate treatment of those with both sets of problems can substantially improve their everyday life.

Although ADHD and Asperger syndrome are separate and different syndromes, multiple research studies have demonstrated that a significant percentage of those

DOI: 10.4324/9781003141976-22

on the autism spectrum, including Asperger syndrome, also have executive function impairments associated with ADHD (Van dcr Meer, Oerlemans, Steijn et al., 2012; Sinzig, Walter, and Doepfner, 2009). On the other side, multiple studies have also shown that a significant percentage of children and adults diagnosed with ADHD also demonstrate characteristics of autism spectrum/Asperger syndrome.

Exact percentages of overlap vary widely from study to study depending on the sample and measures used to define ADHD and autism spectrum. A meta-analysis overview by Demetriou et al. (2017) indicated that broad executive dysfunction has been found in multiple studies of those with autism spectrum disorder and that these executive functions impairments tend to be relatively stable across development of those on the spectrum.

Reviewing multiple studies, Grzadzinski et al. (2010) summarized prevalence of ADHD symptoms in individuals with a primary diagnosis of autism spectrum disorder as ranging from 13% to 50% in studies of those in the general community. Prevalence of ADHD symptoms found in studies of clinical samples of children diagnosed with autism spectrum disorder was considerably higher, between 20% and 85%. This wide range of variability is likely due to differences in the measures utilized in the clinical studies and to variability in the cognitive levels of those being evaluated.

More than a few research studies have demonstrated that half to two-thirds or more of those diagnosed with the "higher functioning" form of Autism Spectrum Disorder (previously known as Asperger Syndrome) also have ADHD (Tsai, 2013; Lecavalier et al., 2019). Joshi et al. (2014) reported that up to three fourths of clinically referred persons with autism spectrum disorder suffer from significant ADHD symptoms. Yet many of those individuals diagnosed with Autism Spectrum Disorder do not receive assessment or treatment for ADHD which might significantly improve their functioning in daily life and may improve their ability to benefit from education.

One study done at the Children's National Medical Center demonstrated that children with ASD tend to demonstrate not only weaker, but worsening scores relative to age norms on "real world" measures of executive functions as they get older (Rosenthal et al., 2013). That study utilized not laboratory neuropsychological tests of executive functions, but parent reports using the BRIEF rating scale, a frequently used normed measure for ADHD-related impairments of executive function. That scale queries about everyday tasks such as ability to get started on assignments, to organize materials, and to utilize working memory in a variety of tasks required of all students. As they became older, those "higher functioning" children with ASD tended to get further behind norms for their age in a variety of executive functions. The authors of that study noted:

> there is a widening divergence from the normative sample in … executive abilities in children with ASD as they age. This has implications for the challenges faced by high-functioning individuals with ASD as they attempt to enter mainstream work and social environments.
>
> (Rosenthal et al., 2013, p. 13)

A study by Karalunas et al. (2018) compared almost 1000 children aged 5 to 17 years on six measures of executive function. Five hundred nine had ADHD, 97 were on the Autism Spectrum without intellectual disability, and 301 were typically developing controls. The ADHD and Autism spectrum groups showed virtually the same results in most areas of executive functions tested, even when the researchers controlled for symptom severity, hyperactivity, or communication challenges across the ADHD and autism groups.

The same study (Karalunas et al., 2018) demonstrated the importance of recognizing that there are both overlapping and some unique cognitive impairments in ADHD and Autism spectrum disorder without intellectual disability. However, they found that those children with both ADHD and Autism syndrome disorder tended to be the most impaired of the mixed groups studied. Miodovnik et al. (2015) showed that often children who have both ADHD symptoms and symptoms of Autism spectrum disorder, may be recognized as having ADHD, but may not be noticed and identified as having Autism spectrum disorder.

One study done at Harvard found that 76% of 107 children and adolescents diagnosed with autism spectrum disorder, most with IQ scores within or above the average range, also fully met diagnostic criteria for ADHD. Importantly, they also reported that of those youths found to have ADHD as well as Autism spectrum disorder 41% had never previously received appropriate assessment or treatment for their ADHD (Joshi et al., 2014).

This led those researchers to issue a warning:

> failure to recognize ADHD—especially in intellectually capable youth with autism spectrum disorder can seriously undermine educational and social functioning, worsening already compromised social performance and can predispose these youth to increased risk for disruptive disorders, mood dysregulation, and substance use disorder.
>
> (Joshi et al., 2014, p. 847)

Another recent study, this one at Children's Hospital of Philadelphia, demonstrated that children on the autism spectrum who exhibit symptoms of ADHD, even if they do not meet full criteria for ADHD, tend to have significantly more difficulty with adaptive behavior in school, home and community and tend to benefit from ADHD treatments (Yerys et al., 2019). These data suggest that regardless of the exact percentage of those on the autism spectrum, it is important for those treating individuals on the autism to screen for possible ADHD impairments and to provide appropriate treatment when such symptoms are found, whether or not all official diagnostic criteria for ADHD are apparent. Similar observations were reported by Sprenger, Bühler, Poustka et al. (2013).

A study of 99 children aged 6 to 13 years with Autism spectrum disorder found that the presence of ADHD in a child with ASD increased the vulnerability of that child to other psychiatric symptoms such as depression, anxiety, and obsessive compulsive disorder and that greater severity of those ADHD symptoms tended to be associated with greater severity of such comorbid symptoms (Mansour et al., 2017).

Autistic Traits in Children with ADHD

A 2013 study at Harvard demonstrated the importance of clinicians being alert to Autistic traits in children diagnosed with ADHD, but not diagnosed with Autism. Using an established measure to pick up autistic traits such as being excessively withdrawn or having social problems or thought problems without an existing diagnosis of Autism spectrum, the Harvard researchers found that 18% of their sample of children diagnosed with ADHD also suffered from autistic traits that were associated with greater severity of illness and more impaired dysfunction that those with ADHD alone (Kotte et al., 2013).

A more recent study from a large national data set including more than 2000 children diagnosed with ADHD found that approximately one of eight children diagnosed with ADHD (12.5%) also met diagnostic criteria for autism spectrum disorder (Zablotsky et al., 2020). That study concluded that children diagnosed with both ADHD and autism spectrum disorder have more treatment needs and co-occurring psychopathology than children with ADHD alone (Zablotsky et al., 2020, p. 94).

An international study of 821 children with ADHD and 1050 of their siblings found more symptoms of autism in children with ADHD than in their siblings or typical controls. That study identified five different types of ADHD in regard to autism symptoms. One group with ADHD had very few autism symptoms. At the other extreme was a group with ADHD who had symptoms of comorbid language disorder, oppositional defiant disorder, increased motor disorder, and/or conduct disorder. Members of that group demonstrated more autism symptoms than those with less complicated ADHD (Mulligan, Anney, O'Regan et al., 2008).

ADHD in Itself is Often Complicated in a Variety of Ways

Researchers and clinicians specializing in ADHD have attempted to deal with variability among patients with ADHD by highlighting accompanying co-occurring (comorbid) disorders. The Multi-Modal Treatment Study of ADHD enrolled 579 children ages 7 to 9 years and found that 70% of those children fully met diagnostic criteria for at least one additional psychiatric disorder (Jensen et al., 2001).

Table 16.1 shows results from a large study involving 61,000 children aged 6 to 17 years where those children who had ADHD had much higher rates for other disorders than did children who did not have ADHD. Among the children in the ADHD group 33% had at least one additional psychiatric or learning disorder, 16% had 2, and 18% had 3 or more (Larson et al., 2007).

Co-occurring disorders are also very common among adults with ADHD. A nationally representative study of adults with ADHD aged 18 to 44 years, not referred for treatment, found that those with ADHD were 6.2 times more

Table 16.1 Psychiatric Disorders Diagnosed in Children with and without ADHD

	ADHD %	*Non-ADHD %*
Learning Disorder	46.1	5.3
Conduct Disorder	27.4	1.8
Anxiety	17.8	2.3
Depression	13.9	1.4
Autism Spectrum Disorder	6.0	0.6

Source: Larson et al. (2007)

Table 16.2 Prevalence and Odds Ratios for Psychiatric Disorders in Adults with ADHD

	Lifetime Prevalence	*Odds Ratio*
Mood Disorders	38.3	5.0
Anxiety Disorders	47.1	3.7
Substance Use Disorders	15.2	3.0
Impulse Disorders	19.6	3.7

Source: Kessler et al. (2006)

likely to have had at least one additional psychiatric disorder at some point in their life than adults without ADHD (Kessler et al., 2005, 2006).

Table 16.2 reports data from a study of adults with ADHD. An odds ratio of 1.0 indicates that prevalence of that disorder is that same for persons with ADHD as for persons of similar age in the general population. 3.0 indicates three times the base rate of persons the same age in the general population. That study showed that adults with ADHD were 6.2 times more likely to have at least one psychiatric disorder in their lifetime than were adults without ADHD.

More details about co-occurring disorders in ADHD are provided in my edited book, *ADHD Comorbidities: Handbook for ADHD Complications in Children and Adults* (Brown, 2009), and my more recent book, *Outside the Box: Rethinking ADD/ADHD in Children and Adults* (Brown, 2017).

Asperger Syndrome is Often Complicated in a Variety of Ways

Those with Asperger syndrome also have been shown to have elevated rates of co-occurring disorders. A large study by Lecavalier et al. (2019) of 658 children with autism spectrum disorder reported the following rates of additional diagnoses in those with IQ above or below the low average range (Table 16.3).

This study of co-occurring disorders in children with autism spectrum disorder did not include obsessive compulsive disorder. However, another study of

Table 16.3 Co-occurring Disorders in 658 Children with Autism Spectrum Disorder

	IQ < 70	*IQ > 70*
ADHD	82.7%	79%
Oppositional Defiant Disorder	51.9%	37.4%
Any Anxiety Disorder	50%	31.9%
Conduct Disorder	10.7%	13.6%
Any mood disorder	9.3%	3.9%

Source: Lecavalier et al. (2019)

children diagnosed with ASD found that 15% of their sample also had obsessive compulsive disorder (Mansour et al., 2017), which has been found to be quite common in adults with autism spectrum disorder whose autistic impairments were not diagnosed until they reached adulthood. Several studies of those adults found about 25% to have OCD while many others had various obsessions or compulsions that were problematic, but not severe enough fully to meet OCD diagnostic criteria (see studies listed in Corrêa and Gaag, 2017, p. 135). It seems likely that some of the 25% of adults with autism spectrum disorder who have OCD probably have had onset in childhood or early adolescence.

A more recent study assessed 1272 children aged 6 to 17 years from the Autism Speaks Treatment Network Consortium to see how many were reported by parents to have had a diagnosis of depression vs. how many were reported by parents as never having been diagnosed with depression (Green-lee, Mosley, Shui et al., 2016). Among those children 6 to 12 years old 4.8% were reported to have had a diagnosis of depression. The incidence of depression in children aged 13–17 years old was much higher: 20.2%.

Factors associated with higher rates of depression were being older than 12 years, having higher IQ, and having a diagnosis of Asperger disorder. These data suggest that early adolescent children with higher IQ and an autism spectrum diagnosis are more vulnerable than younger children to having depression serious enough to be clinically diagnosed.

Another study in the U.K. reported a similar result from 396 children diagnosed with autism spectrum disorder (Hosozawa, Sacker, and Cable, 2020). They found that children who were not diagnosed with autism until after age 11 years were reported to have more depressive symptoms and more self-harming behaviors than those children whose autism characteristics had been recognized and diagnosed between ages 7 and 11 years.

One possibility is that those children with autism spectrum who were older and brighter were burdened with stronger feelings of inadequacy relative to their peers and more hopelessness about their future. This is a group of children who have special need for support to help them develop their potential and cope more effectively with their limitations.

Another type of co-occurring disorder not included in the Lecavalier et al. (2019) study was problems with sleep. Multiple studies reviewed by Cortesi et al. (2010) indicated that significant percentages of children on the autism spectrum (40–80%) have chronic problems with sleep onset, intermittent awakening, and short sleep duration according to parental report, sometimes confirmed by actigraphy or polysomnography. That review argues that short sleep duration is often associated with increases in daytime social skill deficits, stereotypic behavior and increases in other symptoms of ASD.

Another important concern is the rate of suicidal concerns among those on the autism spectrum. Cassidy et al. (2018) reviewed reports indicating elevated rates of suicidality in adults diagnosed with autism spectrum conditions. Their survey of adults with autism spectrum conditions (ASC) found that 72% scored above the recommended cutoff on a suicide risk scale as compared to 33% of adults in the general population. In another study of adults diagnosed with Asperger syndrome, 66% had contemplated suicide while reports from the general population were at 17%. Of those with Asperger syndrome participating in the study 38% had made at least one suicide attempt in their lifetime; rate in the general population on this measure was 8%.

Among a sample of 791 children aged 1 to 16 years with autism the reported rate of suicidal thoughts or suicidal attempts was substantially higher than the rate of typical children. For those children with autism, the four variables influencing this higher rate were: age 10 years or older; Black or Hispanic; lower socio-economic strata; and male. Comorbid psychological problems most predictive of suicidal thoughts or attempts were: depression, behavior problems and having been teased (Mayes, Gorman, Hilwig-Garcia, and Syed, 2013).

Multiple Differences Complicate Both ADHD and Asperger Syndrome

Data in this chapter indicate that many, though not all, persons with Asperger syndrome also have significant aspects of the executive function impairments of ADHD, if not the full syndrome. These data also show that a smaller, but significant number of persons with ADHD also have at least some traits of Asperger syndrome, if not the full syndrome. Presented data also show that those with ADHD and those with Asperger syndrome tend to have complications from co-occurring learning or psychiatric disorders, each of which may vary in intensity over time.

The main point here is that ADHD and Asperger syndrome are not watertight compartments, not isolated silos. Rather, many affected persons have overlap between some or all of the features of both disorders. Moreover, overlap between those two disorders is often further complicated by overlaps with other disorders such as anxiety, depression, substance use disorders, OCD, learning disorders, etc.

In addition, there is evidence suggesting that the presence of ADHD with ASD appears to bring an increased risk of further complications by additional co-occurring disorders. This was demonstrated in a study by Gordon-Lipkin et al. (2018), which showed that when a child with ASD has co-occurring ADHD, that child tends to have a 2.2-fold increased risk of also having an anxiety disorder and a 2.72-fold increased risk of having a mood disorder relative to a child with ASD who does not have ADHD.

These complications on complications highlight the need for personalized diagnosis and personalized treatments designed for each individual in all of his or her particular complexities of strengths and difficulties. There are many examples of these complexities in the twelve cases in this book.

17 Summary Observations and Resources

Each of this book's twelve chapters about individuals includes reflections on that person's situation and my efforts to provide support and treatment for them. This chapter offers information and reflections about factors that seem important for many of the children, teens and adults described here as having both ADHD and Asperger Syndrome. Some of this information might be useful for adaptation and use with other children, teens, or adults with similar difficulties. Following this information is a listing of books that offer additional information and support.

1 **Correct diagnosis of ADHD and/or Asperger syndrome is often missed.** Many pediatricians, psychologists, psychiatrists and other medical or mental health specialists do not receive adequate up-to-date training for recognizing and treating those with ADHD and/or Asperger syndrome. As a result, some children, teens, and adults with these challenges are not correctly diagnosed and may be given treatment which is not helpful and may exacerbate their difficulties. It is helpful to seek out a clinician experienced in dealing with these difficulties, at least for initial evaluation, so that appropriate treatment and support is not delayed.

2 **Each person with ADHD usually is able to exercise their executive functions quite well for a few specific activities or tasks that especially interest them while they often are unable to muster the same efforts and abilities for many other tasks they need to do and may want to do.** This makes ADHD appear to be a simple lack of willpower when it is actually a problem with the dynamics of the chemistry of the brain which usually requires use of medication for ADHD, just as impairments of vision often require use of eyeglasses or contact lenses.

3 **Developing recognition of one's strengths and difficulties helps social relationships.** Stories of Joshua (Chapter 2) and Sam (Chapter 3) illustrate how a child who learns to see self as very bright or exceptionally talented can develop a condescending attitude or "know it all" behavior that often irritates peers and provokes rejection or bullying, especially if they lack

DOI: 10.4324/9781003141976-23

appreciation for strengths and limitations of others. Often those with ADHD and/or Asperger syndrome need extra coaching to recognize how comments to their peers may be well-intended, yet annoying.

4   **Collaboration with staff in primary and secondary schools can be helpful so long as parents are engaged and not excessively demanding.** Teachers usually appreciate parents providing them information in advance about unusual vulnerabilities or limitations of students. However, it is important for parents to recognize that teachers are dealing with groups of students and are limited in how much they can arrange activities and teaching strategies to meet all needs of every student and they cannot control all of the interactions between students in group activities. The story of Justin (Chapter 6) illustrates how school staff can be very helpful in facilitating adjustment of students with ADHD and Asperger syndrome in school.

5   **Many of those with ADHD also have additional learning problems, emotional or behavioral impairments** such as anxiety, depression, obsessive-compulsive disorder, or sleep disorders which require attention and, perhaps, treatment. The stories of Jeremy (Chapter 5), Anthony (Chapter 7), Drew (Chapter 8), Sandra (Chapter 9), Loretta (Chapter 12), and Gary (Chapter 13) illustrate various combinations of ADHD and/Asperger syndrome with various other disorders. Detailed information about various co-occurring disorders often found with ADHD and how they modify treatment needs is available in two of my books: *ADHD Comorbidities: Handbook for ADHD Complications in Children and Adults* (Brown, 2009); and *Outside the Box: Rethinking ADD/ADHD in Children and Adults* (Brown, 2017).

6   **Balance between support and confrontation rather than parental polarization is helpful.** Sam's story (Chapter 3) illustrates how parents of smart children with ADHD and Asperger syndrome can help one another to maintain a reasonable balance between supporting and protecting their child vs. confronting and disciplining the child to teach him what behaviors are unacceptable to them or to others. It is easy for parents to polarize with one parent emphasizing the need to provide support while the other repeatedly confronts the child about shortcomings and need to change. Both approaches are needed in balance to adequately help the child.

7   **Those with ADHD and Asperger syndrome (and their parents) can often benefit from learning that these impairments are primarily an inherited difficulty** for which treatment is often effective, if it is appropriately prescribed and adequately "fine-tuned." This may help to reduce self-blame. At the same time these children, teens and adults can also benefit from recognizing and understanding that although they may be quite bright, they still need to invest continuing effort to successfully utilize and develop their abilities. It is not enough just to be smart; sustained effort is also necessary for success.

8   **Home-schooling and specialized schools may provide some protection from bullying for those with Asperger syndrome,** but this separation from interaction with more typical peers, particularly if

prolonged, often makes it more difficult for these students to learn and practice social skills that may be useful and necessary for them as they get older. Stories of Joshua (Chapter 2) and Bella (Chapter 4) illustrate some of these issues.

9   **Medications are often helpful, if adequately "fine-tuned."** Many parents are hesitant to use medications to help their child with ADHD and/or Asperger syndrome (see Chapters 6 and 10). Yet medications are usually quite helpful in treating ADHD impairments and, while there are no medications to treat Asperger syndrome specifically, some medications may be helpful for dealing with anxiety, sleep problems, mood difficulties, obsessive compulsive symptoms, etc. in those with Asperger syndrome. However, many individuals with these difficulties have an exceptionally sensitive body chemistry which requires considerable "fine tuning" of dose and timing to optimize benefits and avoid unpleasant side effects. Medication was one important component of treatment for all of the individuals described in this book while many came for consultation after having considerable difficulty with various medications previously given to them without sufficient "fine-tuning."

10   **Significant misbehavior in childhood needs to be confronted and changed.** If unacceptable behavior is excessively tolerated while appropriate behavior is not adequately rewarded during childhood, it can be very difficult to get change of inappropriate behavior later in those with ADHD and/or Asperger syndrome. The story of Drew (Chapter 8) illustrates how failure to challenge unacceptable behavior during childhood can result in severe difficulties in developing appropriate behavior during adolescence and early adulthood.

11   **Many children and adolescents with ADHD and/or Asperger syndrome struggle with adapting to transitions in their schooling or living situations.** For example, annual change from one grade to another in elementary school, from elementary school to middle school, middle school to high school, high school to college, and from college to work can be quite unsettling for those with ADHD and/or Asperger syndrome unless they are provided careful preparation. The stories of Bella (Chapter 4) and Richard (Chapter 11) illustrate the need for anticipatory support in preparing for such transitions.

12   **Daily help after school from a family member or tutor can be very helpful for students with ADHD and/or Asperger syndrome during elementary and sometimes in secondary school.** For example, the story of Justin (Chapter 6) illustrates how his spending an hour or two with his grandmother almost every day after school provided him a snack, emotional support and structured homework time that was not available to him at home. Often these students need structured supportive time like this more than most other students of similar age.

13   **What kind of psychotherapy is likely to be helpful with children, teens and adults with Asperger syndrome** Exploratory psychotherapy to uncover emotions is often not as helpful to those with Asperger syndrome as

an approach which provides a more didactic, problem-solving approach and, at least sometimes, includes parent participation. Stories of Anthony (Chapter 7), Drew (Chapter 8), Richard (Chapter 11) and others described here show how individualized didactic support can provide opportunity for those with Asperger syndrome to learn to use their intellect to understand problematic social interactions and develop "survival skills" which most people without Asperger syndrome usually pick up without explicit teaching, by simply observing social interactions of others.

14 **Those with social anxiety or Asperger syndrome often need encouragement or a "loving push" to help them approach a teacher or professor during office hours, to ask a question during class, or to reach out to classmates to form informal study groups to prepare for tests or examinations.** The story of Anthony (Chapter 10) describes a way that a student can form a small study group to prepare for tests or exams and, in the process make some new friends.

15 **Because they have difficulty in identifying and talking about their emotions, those with Asperger syndrome often need help to raise and address emerging concerns** such as marital conflicts between parents, sibling bullying, sexuality and pubescent development, or health problems or death of family members or friends. Sometimes parents can help with this, in other situations help from a counselor or therapist may be needed. Stories about Jeremy (Chapter 5) and Justin (Chapter 6) illustrate these difficulties.

16 **Some adolescents and adults with Asperger syndrome have powerfully conflicting feelings about developing or continuing emotionally close emotional relationships with others.** Some parents and counselors respond by trying to push the individual one way or the other to do what they feel would be best for their son, daughter or client. Unless the possible relationship presents a clearly evident threat, it is usually preferable for the parent or counselor to try to help the adolescent or adult to explore their conflicting feelings and the reasons for them without trying to push for one specific outcome or another. The story of Loretta (Chapter 12) provides an example of such conflicts.

17 **Full neuropsychological testing is not usually necessary or especially helpful for assessment of ADHD and/or Asperger syndrome.** Usually a semi-structured interview with the student and parents done by a clinician experienced with these syndromes is the most important element of an effective evaluation. In addition, normed rating scales like the *Behavior Rating Inventory of Executive Function* (BRIEF) (Guy et al., 2004; Roth et al., 2005) and the *Brown Executive Function/Attention Rating Scales* (BEFARS) (Brown, 2019) provide specific standardized measures for ADHD impairments at various age levels. *The Social Responsiveness Scale–2* (SRS-2) (Constantino and Gruber, 2012) and the *Gilliam Autism Rating Scale* (GARS-3) (Gilliam, 2014) are normed measures that may be helpful in assessing for Asperger Syndrome.

18 **Parents with a son or daughter who has Asperger syndrome often suffer from persisting disappointment** because that son or daughter may have considerable difficulty in showing affection for their parents and more often than most other sons or daughters do not take into account the feelings of their parents. It is important for those parents to be helped to understand that this neglect is not usually due to lack of affection for the parents but to difficulty in maintaining awareness of and being able to express such concerns. The story of Jorge (Chapter 8) illustrates these issues.

19 **The PEERS treatment program developed by Elizabeth Laugeson and colleagues at UCLA offers a systematic, evidence-based program of resources** to help teens (Laugeson and Frankel, 2010) and young adults (Laugeson, 2017) with Asperger syndrome and other autism spectrum disorders develop practical skills for social interactions. These materials are designed for use with small group treatment programs in schools or clinics, but the materials can also be adapted for individualized use by clinicians and parents.

20 **Current scientific evidence estimates that ADHD prevalence in the U.S. is currently at 10.2% of children aged 4 to 17 years.** Some feel that this increase of more than 4% since 1997–1998 is due to overdiagnosis, but that assumption is challenged by these new data. It has also been shown that ADHD impairments tend to persist through adolescence or beyond in more than 70% of boys and girls diagnosed with ADHD in childhood.

21 **Current research has also reported a substantial increase in the percentage of children diagnosed with autism in the U.S.— now 1 in 59, a 15% increase from the estimate of 1 in 68 from research two years earlier.** Other data suggest that about 44% of those diagnosed with autism have IQ in the average or above average range. This book focuses on those diagnosed with autism in that higher IQ range which previously was identified as Asperger syndrome.

22 **Multiple research studies have demonstrated that half to two-thirds of those with average or above average IQ who have been diagnosed with autism also have impairments of executive functions characteristic of ADHD.**

23 **Although challenges faced by those with ADHD and Asperger syndrome can be very frustrating and discouraging to them and to their families, many stories in this book illustrate how persistent effort, patience, and utilization of available resources can often bring significant improvement over time.**

Further Reading

Ariel, C. N. (2012). *Loving someone with Asperger's syndrome: Understanding & connecting with your partner.* Oakland, CA: New Harbinger Publications.

Baker, J., & Myers, J. M. (2013). *No more victims: Protecting those with autism from cyber bullying, Internet predators, & scams.* Arlington, TX: Future Horizons.

Baker, J. (2001). *The social skills picture book: Teaching play, emotion, and communication to children with autism.* Arlington, TX: Future Horizons.

Baker, J. (2005). *Preparing for life.* Arlington, TX: Future Horizons.

Baker, J. (2001). *The social skills picture book: Teaching play, emotion, and communication to children with autism.* Arlington, TX: Future Horizons.

Baker, J. (2006). *The social skills picture book for high school and beyond.* Arlington, TX: Future Horizons.

Baker, J. (2008). *No more meltdowns.* Arlington, TX: Future Horizons.

Bashe, P. R. (2014). *Asperger Syndrome: The oasis guide: Advice, inspiration, insight, and hope from early intervention to adulthood.* New York: Harmony Books.

Bernier, R., Dawson, G., & Nigg, J. T. (2020). *What science tells us about autism spectrum disorder: Making the right choices for your child.* New York: The Guilford Press.

Berninger, V. W., & Richards, T. L. (2007). *Brain literacy for educators and psychologists.* Amsterdam: Elsevier.

Bissonnette, B. (2013). *The complete guide to getting a job for people with Asperger's syndrome: Find the right career and get hired.* London: Jessica Kingsley.

Boroson, B. (2016). *Autism spectrum disorder in the inclusive classroom.* New York: Scholastic.

Brown, J. T., Wolf, L. E., King, L., & Kukiela Bork, G. R. (2012). *The parent's guide to college for students on the autism spectrum.* Shawnee Mission, KS: AAPC Publishing.

Brown, T. E. (2005). *Attention deficit disorder: The unfocused mind in children and adults.* New Haven, CT: Yale University Press.

Brown, T. E. (2013). *A new understanding of ADHD in children and adults: Executive function impairments.* New York: Routledge, Taylor & Francis Group.

Brown, T. E., (2014) *Smart but stuck: Emotions in teens and adults with ADHD.* San Francisco: Jossey-Bass/Wiley.

Brown, T. E. (2017). *Outside the box: Rethinking ADD/ADHD in children and adults: A practical guide.* Arlington, VA: American Psychiatric Association Publishing.

Gaus, V. L. (2011). *Living well on the spectrum: How to use your strengths to meet the challenges of Asperger syndrome/high-functioning autism.* New York: The Guilford Press.

Grandin, T., & Johnson, C. (2006). *Animals in translation using the mysteries of autism to decode animal behavior.* Orlando, FL: Harcourt.

Grandin, T. (2006). *Thinking in pictures: And other reports from my life with autism.* New York: Vintage.

Grandin, T. (2014). *The way I see it: A personal look at autism & Asperger's.* Arlington, TX: Future Horizons.

Grandin, T., & Barron, S. (2016). *Unwritten rules of social relationships: Decoding social mysteries through autism's unique perspectives.* Arlington, TX: Future Horizons, Incorporated.

Grandin, T., & Johnson, C. (2006). *Animals in translation: Using the mysteries of autism to decode animal behavior.* Orlando, FL: Harcourt.

Grandin, T., & Moore, D. (2015). *The loving push: How parents and professionals can help spectrum kids become successful adults.* Arlington, TX: Future Horizons.

Grandin, T., & Panek, R. (2014). *The autistic brain: Helping different kinds of minds succeed.* Boston, MA: Houghton Mifflin Harcourt.

Grandin, T., & Moore, D. (2015). *The loving push: How parents and professionals can help spectrum kids become successful adults.* Arlington, TX: Future Horizons.

Greene, R. W. (2014). *The explosive child: A new approach for understanding and parenting easily frustrated, chronically inflexible children.* New York: Harper.

Grossberg, B. N. (2015). *Asperger's and adulthood: A guide to working, loving, and living with Asperger's syndrome.* Berkeley, CA: Althea Press.

Jackson, L. (2006). *Freaks, geeks and Asperger syndrome: A user guide to adolescence.* London: Jessica Kingsley.

Jackson, L. (2017). *Sex, drugs and Asperger's syndrome: A user guide to adulthood.* London: Jessica Kingsley.

Kim, C. (2015). *Nerdy, shy, and socially inappropriate: A user guide to an Asperger life.* Philadelphia, PA: Jessica Kingsley.

Klass, P., & Costello, E. (2004). *Quirky kids: Understanding and helping your child who doesn't fit in —when to worry and when not to worry.* New York: Ballantine Books.

Kutscher, M. L., Attwood, T., & Wolff, R. R. (2007). *Kids in the syndrome mix of ADHD, LD, Asperger's, Tourette's, bipolar, and more! The one stop guide for parents, teachers, and other professionals.* London: Jessica Kingsley Publishers.

Laugeson, E. A. (2013). *The science of making friends helping socially challenged teens and young adults.* San Francisco, CA: Jossey-Bass.

Laugeson, E. A. (2017). *PEERS for young adults: Social skills training for adults with autism spectrum disorder and other social challenges.* New York: Routledge.

Laugeson, E. A., & Frankel, F. (2010). *Social skills for teenagers with developmental and autism spectrum disorders: The PEERS treatment manual.* New York: Routledge.

Lovett, J. P. (2005). *Solutions for adults with Asperger syndrome: Maximizing the benefits, minimizing the drawbacks to achieve success.* Gloucester, MA: Fair Winds Press.

Marshall, T. A. (2015). *I am aspienwoman: The unique characteristics, traits and gifts of adult females on the autism spectrum.* Australia: Tania A. Marshall.

Mendes, E. A., & Shore, S. M. (2015). *Marriage and lasting relationships with Asperger's syndrome (autism spectrum disorder): Successful strategies for couples or counselors.* London: Jessica Kingsley.

Mesibov, G. B., Shea, V., & Adams, L. W. (2001). *Understanding Asperger syndrome and high functioning autism.* New York: Kluwer Academic/Plenum.

Meyer, D., & Vadasy, P. (1996). *Living with a brother or sister with special needs: A book for sibs.* Seattle, WA: University of Washington Press.

Myles, B. S., & Southwick, J. (1999). *Asperger syndrome and difficult moments: Practical solutions for tantrums, rage, and meltdowns.* London: Jessica Kingsley.

Najdowski, A. C. (2017). *Flexible and focused: Teaching executive function skills to individuals with autism and attention disorders.* London: Academic Press.

Notbohm, E. (2012). *Ten things every child with autism wishes you knew.* Arlington, TX: Future Horizons Incorporated.

Nowicki, S., & Duke, M. P. (1992). *Helping the child who doesn't fit in.* Atlanta, GA: Peachtree.

Ozonoff, S., Dawson, G., & McPartland, J. (2002). *A parent's guide to Asperger syndrome and high-functioning autism: How to meet the challenges and help your child thrive.* New York: Guilford Press.

Page, T. (2009). Parallel play: *Growing up with undiagnosed Asperger's.* New York: Doubleday.

Prizant, B. M., & Fields-Meyer, T. (2016). *Uniquely human: A different way of seeing autism.* New York: Simon & Schuster Paperbacks.

Robison, J. E. (2008). *Look me in the eye: My life with Asperger's.* New York: Three Rivers Press.

Robison, J. E., & Pascual-Leone, A. (2017). *Switched on: A memoir of brain change and emotional awakening.* New York: Spiegel & Grau.

Silberman, S. (2015). *NeuroTribes.* New York: Penguin Random House.

Simpson, R. L., & McGinnis-Smith, E. (2018). *Social skills success for students with Asperger syndrome and high-functioning autism.* Thousand Oaks, CA: Corwin.

Stumpf, T., & Stumpf, D. S. (2014). *Journal of an ADHD kid: The good, the bad, and the useful.* Bethesda, MD: Woodbine House.

Szatmari, P. (2004). *A mind apart: Understanding children with autism and Asperger syndrome.* New York: Guilford Press.

Taylor, J. F. (2013). *The survival guide for kids with ADHD.* Minneapolis, MN: Free Spirit.

Taylor-Klaus, E. (2020). *The essential guide to raising complex kids with ADHD, anxiety, and more: What parents and teachers really need to know to empower complicated kids with confidence and calm.* Beverly, MA: Fair Winds Press.

Uram, Michael, (2021), *Parenting & Asperger's.* Emeryville, CA. Rockridge Press.

Volkmar, F. R., & Wiesner, L. A. (2009). *A practical guide to autism: What every parent, family member, and teacher needs to know.* Hoboken, NJ: Wiley.

Willey, L. H. (2004). *Asperger syndrome in the family: Redefining normal.* London: Jessica Kingsley.

Willey, L. H., & Attwood, T. (2015). *Pretending to be normal: Living with Asperger's syndrome (autism spectrum disorder).* London: Jessica Kingsley.

Wing, L. (1996). *The autistic spectrum.* London: Constable & Robinson.

Winner, M. G. (2007). *Thinking about you, thinking about me: Teaching perspective taking and social thinking to persons with social cognitive learning challenges.* San Jose, CA: Think Social Publishing.

Wiseman, R. (2014). *Masterminds & and wingmen: Helping our boys cope with schoolyard power, locker-room tests, girlfriends, and the new rules of boy world.* New York: Harmony Books.

Wiseman, R. (2016). *Queen bees & and wannabes: Helping your daughter survive cliques, gossip, boys, and the new realities of girl world.* New York: Harmony.

Wolf, L. E., Brown, J. T., & Bork, G. R. (2009). *Students with Asperger syndrome: A guide for college personnel.* Shawnee Mission, KS: Autism Asperger Pub.

Wylie, P., Beardon, L., & Heath, S. (2014). *Very late diagnosis of Asperger syndrome (autism spectrum disorder): How seeking a diagnosis in adulthood can change your life.* London: Jessica Kingsley.

References

Alvares, G. A., Bebbington, K., Cleary, D., Evans, K., Glasson, E. J., Maybery, M. T., ... Whitehouse, A. J. (2019). The misnomer of "high functioning autism": Intelligence is an imprecise predictor of functional abilities at diagnosis. *Autism*, 24 (1), 221–232. doi:10.1177/1362361319852831.

American Psychiatric Association. (2000). *Diagnostic and statistical manual of mental disorders*, 4th edition [DSM-4]. Washington, DC: American Psychiatric Association.

American Psychiatric Association. (2013). *Diagnostic and statistical manual of mental disorders*, 5th edition [DSM-5]. Washington, DC: American Psychiatric Association.

Antshel, K. M., Zhang-James, Y., Wagner, K. E., Ledesma, A., & Faraone, S. V. (2016). An update on the comorbidity of ADHD and ASD: A focus on clinical management. *Expert Review of Neurotherapeutics*, 16(3), 279–293. doi:10.1586/14737175.2016.1146591.

Aull, E. (2014). *The parent's guide to the medical world of autism: A physician explains diagnosis, medications and treatments*. Arlington, TX: Future Horizons.

Baker, J. (2001). *The social skills picture book: Teaching play, emotion, and communication to children with autism*. Arlington, TX: Future Horizons.

Baker, J. (2005). *Preparing for life*. Arlington, TX: Future Horizons.

Baker, J. (2006). *The social skills picture book for high school and beyond*. Arlington, TX: Future Horizons.

Baker, J. (2008). *No more meltdowns*. Arlington, TX: Future Horizons.

Barkley, R. A. (2006). *Attention-deficit hyperactivity disorder: A handbook for diagnosis and treatment*. New York: Guilford Press.

Barkley, R. A. (2010). Deficient emotional self-regulation: A core component of attention-deficit/hyperactivity disorder. *J. ADHD Related Disorder*, 1(2), 5–37.

Barkley, R. A. (2011a). *Barkley adult ADHD rating scale-IV (BAARS-IV)*. New York: Guilford Press.

Barkley, R. A. (2011b). *Barkley deficits in executive functioning scale (BDEFS)*. New York: Guilford Press.

Barkley, R. A. (2011c). *Barkley functional impairment scale (BFIS)*. New York: Guilford Press.

Barkley, R. A. (2012a). *Barkley deficits in executive functioning scale—children and adolescents (BDEFS-CA)*. New York: Guilford Press.

Barkley, R. A. (2012b). *Barkley functional impairment scale—children and adolescents (BFIS CA)*. New York: Guilford Press.

Barkley, R. A. (2012c). *Executive functions: What they are, how they work, and why they evolved*. New York: Guilford Press.

Barkley, R. A., Murphy, K. R., & Fischer, M. (2008). *ADHD in adults: What the science says*. New York: Guilford Press.

Bar-On, R., Parker, J. D., & Goleman, D. (2000). *The handbook of emotional intelligence: Theory, development, assessment, and application at home, school, and in the workplace*. San Francisco, CA: Jossey-Bass.

Baron-Cohen, S. (1995). *Mindblindness: an essay on autism and theory of mind*. Cambridge, MA: The MIT Press.

Baron-Cohen, S. (2003). *The essential difference: The truth about the male and female brain*. New York: Basic Books.

Baron-Cohen, S., Cosmides, L., & Tooby, J. (2019). *Mindblindness: an essay on autism and theory of mind*. Cambridge, MA: The MIT Press.

Boszormenyi-Nagy, I., & Spark, G. M. (1973). *Invisible loyalties: Reciprocity in intergenerational family therapy*. New York: Harper & Row.

Brown, C. M., Attwood, T., Garnett, M., & Stokes, M. A. (2020). Am I autistic? Utility of the girls questionnaire for autism spectrum condition as an autism assessment in adult women. *Autism in Adulthood*, 2(3), 216–226. doi:10.1089/aut.2019.0054.

Brown, T. E. (2005). *Attention deficit disorder: The unfocused mind in children and adults*. New Haven, CT: Yale University Press.

Brown, T. E. (2006). Executive functions and attention deficit hyperactivity disorder: Implications of two conflicting views. *International Journal of Disability, Development and Education*, 53(1), 35–46.

Brown, T. E. (2009). *ADHD comorbidities: Handbook for ADHD complications in children and adults*. Washington, DC: American Psychiatric Publishing.

Brown, T. E. (2013). *A new understanding of ADHD in children and adults: Executive function impairments*. New York: Routledge.

Brown, T. E., (2014) *Smart but Stuck: Emotions in Teens and Adults with ADHD*. San Francisco, CA: Jossey-Bass/Wiley.

Brown, T. E. (2017). *Outside the box: Rethinking ADD/ADHD in children and adults: A practical guide*. Arlington, VA: American Psychiatric Association Publishing.

Brown, T. E. (2019). *Brown executive function/attention scales manual*. Bloomington, MN: Pearson.

Brown, T. E., Reichel, P. C., & Quinlan, D. M. (2009). Executive function impairments in high IQ adults with ADHD. *Journal of Attention Disorders*, 13(2), 161–167. doi:10.1177/1087054708326113.

Brown, T. E., Reichel, P. C., & Quinlan, D. M. (2011a). Extended time improves reading comprehension test scores for adolescents with ADHD. *Open Journal of Psychiatry*, 1(2), 79–87. doi:10.4236/jsemat.2011.13014.

Brown, T. E., Reichel, P. C., & Quinlan, D. M. (2011b). Executive function impairments in high IQ children and adolescents with ADHD. *Open Journal of Psychiatry*, 1 (2), 56–65. doi:10.4236/ojpsych.2011.12009.

Brugha, T. S. (2018). *The psychiatry of adult autism and Asperger syndrome: A practical guide*. Oxford: Oxford University Press.

Cassidy, S., Bradley, L., Shaw, R., & Baron-Cohen, S. (2018). Risk markers for suicidality in autistic adults. *Molecular Autism*, 9(1). doi:10.1186/s13229-018-0226-4.

Constantino, J. N., & Gruber, C. P. (2012). *Social responsiveness scale, second edition (SRS-2)*. Torrance, CA: Western Psychological Services.

Cooper, B., & Widdows, N. (2008). *The social success workbook for teens: Skill-building activities for teens with nonverbal learning disorder, asperger's disorder & other social-skill problems*. Oakland, CA: Instant Help Books.

Corrêa, B. B., & Gaag, R. V. (2017). *Autism spectrum disorders in adults*. Cham, Switzerland: Springer.

Cortesi, F., Giannotti, F., Ivanenko, A., & Johnson, K. (2010). Sleep in children with autistic spectrum disorder. *Sleep Medicine*, 11(7), 659–664. doi:10.1016/j.sleep.2010.01.010.

Cortesi, S. *et al.* (2013). White matter alterations at 33-year follow-up in adults with childhood attention-deficit/hyperactivity disorder. *Biol. Psychiatry*, 74(8), 591–598.

Demetriou, E. A., Lampit, A., Quintana, D. S., Naismith, S. L., Song, Y. J., Pye, J. E., … Guastella, A. J. (2017). Autism spectrum disorders: A meta-analysis of executive function. *Molecular Psychiatry*, 23(5), 1198–1204. doi:10.1038/mp.2017.75.

Denckla, M. B. (2019). *Understanding learning and related disabilities: Inconvenient brains*. New York: Routledge.

Donvan, J., & Zucker, C. (2017). *In a different key: The story of autism*. New York: Broadway Books.

Dweck, C. S. (2008). *Mindset: The new psychology of success*. New York: Ballantine Books.

Fisher, R., Ury, W., & Patton, B. (2011). *Getting to yes: Negotiating agreement without giving in*. New York: Penguin.

Fitzgerald, M., & Bellgrove, M. A. (2006). The overlap between alexithymia and Asperger's syndrome. *Journal of Autism and Developmental Disorders*, 36(4), 573–576. doi:10.1007/s10803-006-0096-z.

Frazier, T. W., Shattuck, P. T., Narendorf, S. C., Cooper, B. P., Wagner, M., & Spitznagel, E. L. (2011). Prevalence and correlates of psychotropic medication use in adolescents with an autism spectrum disorder with and without caregiver-reported attention-deficit/hyperactivity disorder. *Journal of Child and Adolescent Psychopharmacology*, 21(6), 571–579. doi:10.1089/cap.2011.0057.

Gardner, H. (2011). *Frames of mind: The theory of multiple intelligences*. New York: Basic Books.

Gelbar, N. W., Shefcyk, A., & Reichow, B. (2015). A comprehensive survey of current and former college students with autism spectrum disorders. *Yale Journal of Biology and Medicine*, 88, 45–68.

Geller, D. A., & Brown, T. E. (2009). ADHD with Obsessive-compulsive disorder. In T. E. Brown, Ed., *ADHD comorbidities: Handbook for ADHD complications in children and adults* (pp. 177–187). Washington, DC: American Psychiatric Publishing.

Gillberg, C. (1989). Asperger syndrome in 23 Swedish children. *Developmental Medicine & Child Neurology*, 31(4), 520–531. doi:10.1111/j.1469-8749.1989.tb04031.x.

Gillberg, C. (2002). *A guide to Asperger syndrome*. Cambridge: Cambridge University Press.

Gillberg, C., Gillberg, C., Råstam, M., & Wentz, E. (2001). The Asperger syndrome (and high-functioning autism) diagnostic interview (asdi): A preliminary study of a new structured clinical interview. *Autism*, 5(1), 57–66. doi:10.1177/1362361301005001006.

Gilliam, J. E. (2014). *GARS-3: Instructional objectives for individuals who have autism*. Austin, TX: Pro-Ed.

Gioia, G. A., Isquith, P. K., Guy, S. C., & Kenworthy, L. (2000). *BRIEF behavior rating inventory of executive function: Professional manual*. Lutz, FL: Psychological Assessment Resources.

Goldstein, S., Ozonoff, S. (2018). *Assessment of autism spectrum disorders, second edition*. (2018). New York: Guilford Press.

Gordon-Lipkin, E., Marvin, A. R., Law, J. K., & Lipkin, P. H. (2018). Anxiety and mood disorder in children with autism spectrum disorder and adhd. *Pediatrics*, 141 (4). doi:10.1542/peds.2017-1377.

Grandin, T. (2014). *The way I see it: A personal look at autism & Asperger's*. Arlington, TX: Future Horizons.

Greenberg, D. M., Warrier, V., Allison, C., & Baron-Cohen, S. (2018). Testing the empathizing–systemizing theory of sex differences and the extreme male brain theory of autism in half a million people. *Proceedings of the National Academy of Sciences,* 115(48), 12152–12157. doi:10.1073/pnas.1811032115.

Greenlee, J. L., Mosley, A. S., Shui, A. M., Veenstra-Vanderweele, J., & Gotham, K. O. (2016). Medical and behavioral correlates of depression history in children and adolescents with autism spectrum disorder. *Pediatrics,* 137(Supplement). doi:10.1542/peds.2015-2851i.

Grzadzinski, R., Martino, A. D., Brady, E., Mairena, M. A., O'Neale, M., Petkova, E., ... Castellanos, F. X. (2010). Examining autistic traits in children with adhd: Does the autism spectrum extend to adhd? *Journal of Autism and Developmental Disorders,* 41(9), 1178–1191. doi:10.1007/s10803-010-1135-3.

Guan, J., & Li, G. (2017). Injury mortality in individuals with autism. *American Journal of Public Health,* 107(5), 791–793. doi:10.2105/ajph.2017.303696.

Guy, S. C., Isquith, P. K., & Gioia, G. A. (2004). *BRIEF-SR behavior rating inventory of executive function—self-report version.* Lutz, FL: Psychological Assessment Resources.

Handen, B. L., Aman, M. G., Arnold, E., Hyman, S. L., Tumuluru, R. V., Lecavalier, L., ... Smith, T. (2015). Atomoxeting, parent training, and their combination in children with autism spectrum disorder and attention-deficit/hyperactivity disorder. *Journal of American Academy of Child & Adolescent Psychiatry,* 54(11), 905–914.

Harris, J. R., & Pinker, S. (2009). *The nurture assumption: Why children turn out the way they do.* New York: Free Press.

Hénault, I. (2006). *Asperger's Syndrome and sexuality: From adolescence through adulthood.* London: Jessica Kingsley.

Hirvikoski, T., Mittendorfer-Rutz, E., Boman, M., Larsson, H., Lichtenstein, P., & Bölte, S. (2016). Premature mortality in autism spectrum disorder. *British Journal of Psychiatry,* 208(3), 232–238. doi:10.1192/bjp.bp.114.160192.

Hofvander, B.*et al.* (2009). Psychiatric and psychosocial problems in adults with normal-intelligence autism spectrum disorders. *BMC Psychiatry,* 9, 35.

Hollander, E., Hagerman, R., & Fein, D. (2004). *Autism spectrum disorders.* Washington, DC: American Psychiatric Association Publishing.

Hoogman, M.*et al.* (2017). Subcortical brain volume differences in participants with attention-deficit hyperactivity disorder in children and adults: a cross-section mega-analysis. *Lancet Psychiatry,* doi:10.1016/S2215-0366(17)30049-4.

Hosozawa, M., Sacker, A., & Cable, N. (2020). Timing of diagnosis, depression and self-harm in adolescents with autism spectrum disorder. *Autism,* 136236132094554. doi:10.1177/1362361320945540.

Howlin, P. (2004). *Autism and Asperger syndrome: Preparing for adulthood.* London: Routledge.

Jaswal, V. K., & Akhtar, N. (2018). Being versus appearing socially uninterested: Challenging assumptions about social motivation in autism. *Behavioral and Brain Sciences,* 42. doi:10.1017/s0140525x18001826.

Jensen, P. S.*et al.* (2001). ADHD comorbidity findings from the MTA study: comparing comorbid subgroups. *J. Am Acad Child Adoles Psychiatry,* 40(2), 147–158.

Jones, L.*et al.* (2014). Experiences of receiving a diagnosis of autism spectrum disorder: A survey of adults in the United Kingdom. *J. Autism. Dev. Disord.,* 44, 3033–3044.

Joshi, G., Faraone, S. V., Wozniak, J., Tarko, L., Fried, R., Galdo, M., ... Biederman, J. (2014). Symptom profile of ADHD in youth with high-functioning autism spectrum disorder: A comparative study in psychiatrically referred populations. *Journal of Attention Disorders,* 21(10), 846–855. doi:10.1177/1087054714543368.

Joshi, G., Petty, C., Wozniak, J., Henin, A., Fried, R., Galdo, M., ... Biederman, J. (2010). The heavy burden of psychiatric comorbidity in youth with autism spectrum disorders: A large comparative study of a psychiatrically referred population. *Journal of Autism and Developmental Disorders*, 40(11), 1361–1370. doi:10.1007/s10803-010-0996-9.

Joshi, G., Wozniak, J., Petty, C., *et al.* (2013). Psychiatric comorbidity and functioning in a clinically referred population of adults with autism spectrum disorders: a comparative study. *J. Autism. Dev. Disord.*, 43(6), 1314–1325.

Karalunas, S. L., Hawkey, E., Gustafsson, H., Miller, M., Langhorst, M., Cordova, M., ... Nigg, J. T. (2018). Overlapping and distinct cognitive impairments in attention-deficit/hyperactivity and autism spectrum disorder without intellectual disability. *Journal of Abnormal Child Psychology*, 46(8), 1705–1716. doi:10.1007/s10802-017-0394-2.

Kennedy, D. M., & Banks, R. S. (2002). *The ADHD autism connection: A step toward more accurate diagnosis and effective treatment*. Colorado Springs, CO: Waterbrook Press.

Kennedy, R. J., Quinlan, D. M., & Brown, T. E. (2016). Comparison of two measures of working memory impairments in 220 adolescents and adults with ADHD. *Journal of Attention Disorders*, 23(14), 1838–1843.

Kessler, R. C.*et al.* (2005). Patterns and predictors of attention-deficit/hyperactivity disorder persistence into adulthood; results from the National Comorbidity Survey Replication. *Biological Psychiatry*, 57(11), 1442–1451.

Kessler, R. C.*et al.* (2006). The prevalence and correlates of adult ADHD in the United States: results from the National Comorbidity Survey Replication. *Am. J. Psychiatry*, 163(4), 716–723.

Kessler, R. C.*et al.* (2010). Structure and diagnosis of adult attention-deficit/hyperactivity disorder: analysis of expanded symptom criteria from the Adult ADHD Clinical Diagnostic Scale. *Arch. Gen. Psychiatry*, 67(11), 1168–1178.

Kim, C. (2015). *Nerdy, shy, and socially inappropriate: A user guide to an Asperger life*. Philadelphia, PA: Jessica Kingsley.

Kotte, A., Joshi, G., Fried, R., Uchida, M., Spencer, A., Woodworth, K. Y., ... Biederman, J. (2013). Autistic traits in children with and without ADHD. *Pediatrics*, 132 (3). doi:10.1542/peds.2012-3947.

Lai, M., Lombardo, M. V., Chakrabarti, B., & Baron-Cohen, S. (2013). Subgrouping the Autism "Spectrum": Reflections on DSM-5. *PLoS Biology*, 11(4). doi:10.1371/journal.pbio.1001544.

Larson, K.*et al.* (2007). Patterns of comorbidity, functioning and service use for children with ADHD. *Pediatrics*, 127(3), 462–470.

Lawson, R. A., Papadakis, A. A., Higginson, C. I., Barnett, J. E., Wills, M. C., Strang, J. F., ... Kenworthy, L. (2015). Everyday executive function impairments predict comorbid psychopathology in autism spectrum and attention deficit hyperactivity disorders. *Neuropsychology*, 29(3), 445–453. doi:10.1037/neu0000145.

Lecavalier, L., Mccracken, C. E., Aman, M. G., Mcdougle, C. J., Mccracken, J. T., Tierney, E., ... Scahill, L. (2019). An exploration of concomitant psychiatric disorders in children with autism spectrum disorder. *Comprehensive Psychiatry*, 88, 57–64. doi:10.1016/j.comppsych.2018.10.012.

Lehnhardt, F.*et al.* (2016). Sex-related cognitive profile in autism spectrum disorders diagnosed late in life. *J. Autism Devel. Disord.*, 46, 139–154.

Levinson, D. (1978). *Seasons of a man's life*. New York: Knopf.

Logan, S. L., Carpenter, L., Leslie, R. S., Garrett-Mayer, E., Hunt, K. J., Charles, J., & Nicholas, J. S. (2015). Aberrant behaviors and co-occurring conditions as predictors of psychotropic polypharmacy among children with autism spectrum disorders. *Journal of Child and Adolescent Psychopharmacology*, 25(4), 323–336. doi:10.1089/cap.2013.0119.

Lord, C. (2012). A multisite study of the clinical diagnosis of different autism spectrum disorders. *Archives of General Psychiatry*, 69(3), 306–313. doi:10.1001/archgenpsychiatry.2011.148.

Lord, C., & Jones, R. M. (2012). Re-thinking the classification of autism spectrum disorders. *Journal of Child Psychology and Psychiatry*, 53(5), 490–509. doi:10.1111/j.1469-7610.2012.02547.x.

Lundström, S. (2012). Autism spectrum disorders and autisticlike traits. *Archives of General Psychiatry*, 69(1), 46–52. doi:10.1001/archgenpsychiatry.2011.144.

Lundström, S. *et al.* (2012). Autism spectrum disorders and autistic-like traits. *Arch Gen Psychiatry*, 69(1), 46–52.

Mahajan, R., Bernal, M. P., Panzer, R., Whitaker, A., Roberts, W., Handen, B., ... Veenstra-Vanderweele, J. (2012). Clinical practice pathways for evaluation and medication choice for attention-deficit/hyperactivity disorder symptoms in autism spectrum disorders. *Pediatrics*, 130(Supplement 2). doi:10.1542/peds.2012-0900j.

Mansour, R., Dovi, A. T., Lane, D. M., Loveland, K. A., & Pearson, D. A. (2017). ADHD severity as it relates to comorbid psychiatric symptomatology in children with autism spectrum disorders (asd). *Research in Developmental Disabilities*, 60, 52–64. doi:10.1016/j.ridd.2016.11.009.

Marriage, S., Wolverton, A., & Marriage, K. (2009). Autism spectrum disorder grown up: A chart review of adult functioning. *J. Can. Acad. Child Adolesc. Psychiatry*, 18(4), 322–327.

Mattfield, A. T. *et al.* (2014). Brain differences between persistent and remitted attention deficit hyperactivity disorder. *Brain*, 137, 2423–2428.

May, T., Brignell, A., Hawi, Z., Brereton, A., Tonge, B., Bellgrove, M. A., & Rinehart, N. J. (2018). Trends in the overlap of autism spectrum disorder and attention deficit hyperactivity disorder: Prevalence, clinical management, language and genetics. *Current Developmental Disorders Reports*, 5(1), 49–57. doi:10.1007/s40474-018-0131-8.

Mayes, S. D., Calhoun, S. L., Murray, M. J., Morrow, J. D., Yurich, K. K., Mahr, F., ... Petersen, C. (2009). Comparison of scores on the checklist for autism spectrum disorder, childhood autism rating scale, and Gilliam Asperger's disorder scale for children with low functioning autism, high functioning autism, Asperger's disorder, adhd, and typical development. *Journal of Autism and Developmental Disorders*, 39 (12), 1682–1693. doi:10.1007/s10803-009-0812-6.

Mayes, S. D., Calhoun, S. L., Mayes, R. D., & Molitoris, S. (2012). Autism and adhd: Overlapping and discriminating symptoms. *Research in Autism Spectrum Disorders*, 6(1), 277–285. doi:10.1016/j.rasd.2011.05.009.

Mayes, S. D., Gorman, A. A., Hillwig-Garcia, J., & Syed, E. (2013). Suicide ideation and attempts in children with autism. *Research in Autism Spectrum Disorders*, 7(1), 109–119. doi:10.1016/j.rasd.2012.07.009.

McCormick, C., Hepburn, S., Young, G. S., & Rogers, S. J. (2015). Sensory symptoms in children with autism spectrum disorder, other developmental disorders and typical development: A longitudinal study. *Autism*, 20(5), 572–579. doi:10.1177/1362361315599755.

McDougle, C. J. (2013). Sounding a wake-up call: Improving the lives of adults with autism. *Journal of the American Academy of Child & Adolescent Psychiatry*, 52(6), 566–568. doi:10.1016/j.jaac.2013.03.013.

McPartland, J., Klin, A., & Volkmar, F. R. (2014). *Asperger syndrome assessing and treating high-functioning autism spectrum disorders*. New York: Guilford Press.

Miodovnik, A., Harstad, E., Sideridis, G., & Huntington, N. (2015). Timing of the diagnosis of attention-deficit/hyperactivity disorder and autism spectrum disorder. *Pediatrics*, 136(4). doi:10.1542/peds.2015-1502.

Mulligan, A., Anney, R. J., O'Regan, M., Chen, W., Butler, L., Fitzgerald, M., … Gill, M. (2008). Autism symptoms in attention-deficit/hyperactivity disorder: A familial trait which correlates with conduct, oppositional defiant, language and motor disorders. *Journal of Autism and Developmental Disorders*, 39(2), 197–209. doi:10.1007/s10803-008-0621-3.

Mundy, P. C. (2019). Individual differences, social attention, and the history of the social motivation hypotheses of autism. *Behavioral and Brain Sciences*, 42. doi:10.1017/s0140525x18002509.

Politte, L. C., Scahill, L., Figueroa, J., Mccracken, J. T., King, B., & Mcdougle, C. J. (2018). A randomized, placebo-controlled trial of extended-release guanfacine in children with autism spectrum disorder and ADHD symptoms: An analysis of secondary outcome measures. *Neuropsychopharmacology*, 43(8), 1772–1778. doi:10.1038/s41386-018-0039-3.

Pomerantz, E. M., Grolnick, W., & Price, C. E. (2005). The role of parents in how children approach achievement: A dynamic process perspective. In A. J. Elliot & C. S. Dweck, Eds., *Handbook of competence and motivation*, pp. 259–278. New York: Guilford Press.

Pugliese, C. E., Anthony, L., Strang, J. F., Dudley, K., Wallace, G. L., & Kenworthy, L. (2014). Increasing adaptive behavior skill deficits from childhood to adolescence in autism spectrum disorder: Role of executive function. *Journal of Autism and Developmental Disorders*, 45(6), 1579–1587. doi:10.1007/s10803-014-2309-1.

Reichow, B., Volkmar, F. R., & Bloch, M. H. (2013). Systematic review and meta-analysis of pharmacological treatment of the symptoms of attention-deficit/hyperactivity disorder in children with pervasive developmental disorders. *Journal of Autism and Developmental Disorders*, 43(10), 2435–2441. doi:10.1007/s10803-013-1793-z.

Ritvo, R. A., Ritvo, E. R., Guthrie, D., Ritvo, M. J., Hufnagel, D. H., Mcmahon, W., … Eloff, J. (2010). The Ritvo autism Asperger diagnostic scale-revised (raads-r): A scale to assist the diagnosis of autism spectrum disorder in adults: An international validation study. *Journal of Autism and Developmental Disorders*, 41(8), 1076–1089. doi:10.1007/s10803-010-1133-5.

Robison, J. E. (2008). *Look me in the eye: My life with Asperger's*. New York: Three Rivers Press.

Rommelse, N. N., Franke, B., Geurts, H. M., Hartman, C. A., & Buitelaar, J. K. (2010). Shared heritability of attention-deficit/hyperactivity disorder and autism spectrum disorder. *European Child & Adolescent Psychiatry*, 19(3), 281–295. doi:10.1007/s00787-010-0092-x.

Rommelse, N. N., Geurts, H. M., Franke, B., Buitelaar, J. K., & Hartman, C. A. (2011). A review on cognitive and brain endophenotypes that may be common in autism spectrum disorder and attention-deficit/hyperactivity disorder and facilitate the search for pleiotropic genes. *Neuroscience & Biobehavioral Reviews*, 35(6), 1363–1396. doi:10.1016/j.neubiorev.2011.02.015.

Rosenthal, M., Wallace, G. L., Lawson, R., Wills, M. C., Dixon, E., Yerys, B. E., & Kenworthy, L. (2013). Impairments in real-world executive function increase from childhood to adolescence in autism spectrum disorders. *Neuropsychology*, 27(1), 13–18. doi:10.1037/a0031299.

Roth, R. M., Isquith, P. K., & Gioia, G. A. (2005). *BRIEF-A: Behavior rating inventory of executive function - adult version*. Lutz, FL: Psychological Assessment Resources.

Roux, A. M., Shattuck, P. T., Rast, J. E., Rava, J. A., & Anderson, K. A. (2015). *National autism indicators report: Transition into young adulthood*. Philadelphia, PA: A. J. Drexel Autism Institute, Drexel University.

Rumsey, J. M., Rapoport, J. L., & Sceery, W. R. (1985). Autistic children as adults: Psychiatric, social, and behavioral outcomes. *J. American Acad. Child and Adolesc. Psychiatry*, 24(4), 465–473.

Salovey, P., & Mayer, J. D. (1990). Emotional intelligence. *Imagination, Cognition and Personality*, 9(3), 185–211.

Scahill, L., McCracken, J. T., King, B. H., Rockhill, C., Shah, B., Politte, L., … McDougle, C. (2015). Extended-release Guanfacine for hyperactivity in children with autism spectrum disorder. *American Journal of Psychiatry*, 172(12), 1197–1206.

Seltzer, M. M., Lord, C., Swe, A., Orsmond, G., Shattuck, P. T., & Krauss, M. W. (2003). The symptoms of autism spectrum disorders in adolescence and adulthood. *Journal of Autism and Developmental Disorders*, 33(6), 565–581. doi:10.1007/10803.1573-3432.

Shattuck, P. T., Narendorf, S. C., Cooper, B., Sterzing, P. R., Wagner, M., & Taylor, J. L. (2012). Postsecondary education and employment among youth with an autism spectrum disorder. *Pediatrics*, 129(6), 1042–1049. doi:10.1542/peds.2011-2864.

Shaw, P. *et al.* (2007). Attention-deficit/hyperactivity disorder is characterized by a delay in cortical maturation. *Proc. Natl Acad. Sci. USA*, 104(49), 19, 649–619, 654.

Sikora, D. M., Vora, P., Coury, D. L., & Rosenberg, D. (2012). Attention-deficit/hyperactivity disorder symptoms, adaptive functioning, and quality of life in children with autism spectrum disorder. *Pediatrics*, 130(Supplement 2). doi:10.1542/peds.2012-0900g.

Silberman, S. (2015). *NeuroTribes*. New York: Penguin Random House.

Silverstein, M. J., Faraone, S. V., Leon, T. L., Biederman, J., Spencer, T. J., & Adler, L. A. (2018). The relationship between executive function deficits and DSM-5-defined ADHD symptoms. *Journal of Attention Disorders*, 24(1), 41–51. doi:10.1177/1087054718804347.

Sinzig, J., Walter, D., & Doepfner, M. (2009). Attention deficit/hyperactivity disorder in children and adolescents with autism spectrum disorder. *Journal of Attention Disorders*, 13(2), 117–126. doi:10.1177/1087054708326261.

Sprenger, L., Bühler, E., Poustka, L., Bach, C., Heinzel-Gutenbrunner, M., Kamp-Becker, I., & Bachmann, C. (2013). Impact of ADHD symptoms on autism spectrum disorder symptom severity. *Research in Developmental Disabilities*, 34(10), 3545–3552. doi:10.1016/j.ridd.2013.07.028.

Steinhausen, H., & Jakobsen, H. (2019). Incidence rates of treated mental disorders in childhood and adolescence in a complete nationwide birth cohort. *The Journal of Clinical Psychiatry*, 80(3). doi:10.4088/jcp.17m12012.

Tannock, R. & Brown, T. E. (2009). ADHD with language and/or learning disorders in children and adolescents. In T. E. Brown, Ed., *ADHD comorbidities: Handbook for ADHD complications in children and adults* (pp. 189–231). Washington, DC: American Psychiatric Publishing.

Thye, M. D., Bednarz, H. M., Herringshaw, A. J., Sartin, E. B., & Kana, R. K. (2018). The impact of atypical sensory processing on social impairments in autism spectrum disorder. *Developmental Cognitive Neuroscience*, 29, 151–167. doi:10.1016/j.dcn.2017.04.010.

Tincani, M. J., & Bondy, A. (2015). *Autism spectrum disorders in adolescents and adults: Evidence-based and promising interventions*. New York: Guilford Press.

Tsai, L. Y. (2013). Asperger's disorder will be back. *J. Autism Dev. Disorders*, 43, 2914–2942.

Uchida, M., Spencer, T. J., Faraone, S. V., and Biederman, J. (2018) Adult outcome of ADHD: An overview of results from the MGH longitudinal family studies of pediatrically and psychiatrically referred youth with and without ADHD of both sexes. *Journal of Attention Disorders*, 22 (6) 523–534.

Van der Meer, J. M., Lappenschaar, M. G., Hartman, C. A., Greven, C. U., Buitelaar, J. K., & Rommelse, N. N. (2014). Homogeneous combinations of ASD–ADHD traits and their cognitive and behavioral correlates in a population-based sample. *Journal of Attention Disorders*, 21(9), 753–763. doi:10.1177/1087054714533194.

Van der Meer, J. M., Oerlemans, A. M., Steijn, D. J., Lappenschaar, M. G., Sonneville, L. M., Buitelaar, J. K., & Rommelse, N. N. (2012). Are Autism Spectrum Disorder and Attention-Deficit/Hyperactivity Disorder different manifestations of one overarching disorder? Cognitive and symptom evidence from a clinical and population-based sample. *Journal of the American Academy of Child & Adolescent Psychiatry*, 51(11), 1160–1172. doi:10.1016/j.jaac.2012.08.024.

Ventura, P., Giambattista, C. D., Spagnoletta, L., Trerotoli, P., Cavone, M., Gioia, A. D., & Margari, L. (2020). Methylphenidate in autism spectrum disorder: A long-term follow up naturalistic study. *Journal of Clinical Medicine*, 9(8), 2566. doi:10.3390/jcm9082566.

Volkmar, F., Ed. (2019). *Autism and pervasive developmental disorders*, 3rd edition. Cambridge: Cambridge University Press.

Volkmar, F. R., & Wiesner, L. A. (2018). *Essential clinical guide to understanding and treating autism*. Hoboken, NJ: Wiley.

Wallace, G. L.*et al.* (2015). Longitudinal cortical development during adolescence and young adulthood in autism spectrum disorder: increased cortical thinning but comparable surface area changes. *J. Am. Acad. Child Adolesc. Psychiatry*, 54(6), 464–469.

Wehman, P., Smith M. D., & Schall, C. (2009). *Autism & the transition to adulthood: Success beyond the classroom*. Baltimore, MD: Paul H. Brookes Publishing Co.

Waterhouse, L. (2013). *Rethinking autism: Variation and complexity*. Amsterdam, Netherlands: Elsevier.

Wilens, T. E., & Hammerness, P. G. (2016). *Straight talk about psychiatric medications for kids*, 4th edition. New York: Guilford Press.

Wilens, T. E., Robertson, B., Sikirica, V., Harper, L., Young, J. L., Bloomfield, R., ... Cutler, A. J. (2015). A randomized, placebo-controlled trial of Guanfacine extended release in adolescents with attention-deficit/hyperactivity disorder. *Journal of American Academy of Child & Adolescent Psychiatry*, 54(11), 916–925.

Wolraich, M. L., Hagan, J. F., Allan, C., Chan, E., Davison, D., Earls, M., ... Zurhellen, W. (2019). Clinical practice guideline for the diagnosis, evaluation, and treatment of attention-deficit/hyperactivity disorder in children and adolescents. *Pediatrics*, 144(4). doi:10.1542/peds.2019-2528.

World Health Organization. 2018. International Statistical Classification of Diseases and Related Health Problems, 11th revision [ICD-11]. Retrieved from http://apps.who.int/classifications/icd10/browse/2016/en.

Yerys, B. E.*et al.* (2019). Functional connectivity of fronto-parietal and salience/ventral attention networks have independent associations with co-occurring ADHD symptoms in children with autism. *Biol. Psychiatry Cogn. Neurosci. Neuroimaging*, 4(4), 343–351.

Zablotsky, B., Bramlett, M. D., & Blumberg, S. J. (2020). Co-occurrence of autism spectrum disorder in children with ADHD. *J. Attention Disorders*, 24(1), 94–103.

Index

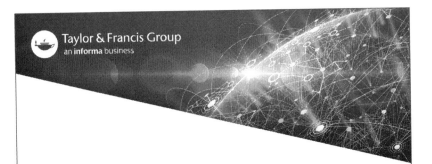